Terror
Below the Wind

Terror
Below the Wind

A Soldier's Story
Borneo 1961–1964

by

Mike Jacobs

Librario

Published by

Librario Publishing Ltd.

ISBN 10:
ISBN 13:

Copies can be ordered via the Internet
www.librario.com

or from:

Brough House, Milton Brodie, Kinloss
Moray IV36 2UA
Tel/Fax No 00 44 (0)1343 850 617

Printed and bound by 4edge Limited, Hockley. www.4edge.co.uk

Typeset by 3btype.com

Contents

Formed
24th June 2006
HM Forces, Commonwealth Forces,
Merchant Navy
Federation of Malaya Police
The Civil Service
St John Ambulance Brigade
And all Auxiliary Forces
In all Malaya/Borneo/Brunei/Singapore theatre during the Second
World War, the Malayan Emergency;
The Dutch East Indies Insurrection (Java/Sumatra);
The Brunei Insurrection; The Borneo/Indonesian Confrontation
and all thereafter.

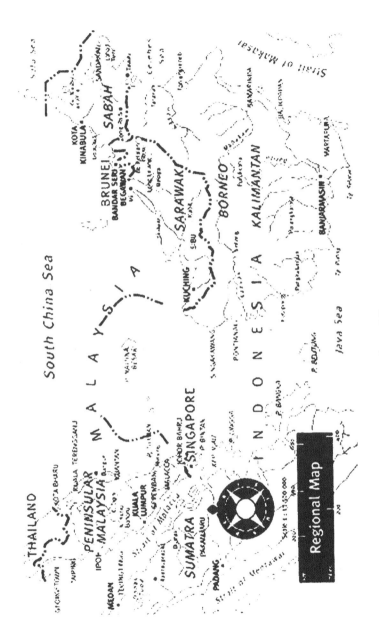

Area of Operations

8

Terror below the Wind

This is my story

*The story tells of a group of pals and the adventures they
encountered whilst on service in the Far East.
Wild nights in downtown Singapore's gangland;
Anti-piracy patrols; head hunters; the discovery of Japanese soldiers
16 years after WWII.*

December 1962

*Rebellion in Brunei, and the rescue of hostages
Long distance patrolling of the Indonesian frontier, and the
discovery of Japanese war gold.
A cynical twist, forty years later, in 1994 on a holiday to
Singapore and a chance meeting.
The last adventure to find the gold and fight our way out
through pirate infested waters.*

*This story is based on fact, although the author has added
much for the enjoyment of the reader.
Now it is up to you the reader to decide what is fact
and what is fiction.*

The Queen's Own Highlanders (Seaforth and Camerons) rehearse de-planing on the fight-deck of the aircraft-carrier HMS Bulwark *for the assault on Seria, December 1962.*

The Battle for Brunei, December 1962

The 1st Battalion Queen's Own Highlanders (Seaforth and Cameron)

On 8th December 1962 there was a revolt in the Sultanate of Brunei, where rebels attacked the Sultan's Palace and other government establishments. The rebels took many hostages and seized the Shell Oilfields at a place called Seria.

The Battalion was tasked to deal with the problem. Neutralise the rebels – free the hostages.

Alpha Company moved from Singapore by air, while Bravo Company sailed at full speed on HMS *Cavalier*.

Alpha Company carried out the air assault, catching the rebels by surprise. The author, then an eighteen year old, was the third man to jump from the Beverly aircraft as it was still rolling, and immediately engage the rebels.

After a swift battle, the Battalion cleared Seria and freed 46 hostages without loss to our troops.

The Battalion returned to Borneo in May 1993 to carry out long range patrolling of the Indonesian border, and to train local tribesmen as border scouts, a task that is still carried out today, with that other famous Regiment from Hereford.

A Survivor of the Brunei Rebellion tells her story ...

I am sorry it took so long to find you guys but I could not until recently, look back at the events of December 1962 and the horror of that time. Finally, I found a news article about your regiment, The Queen's Own Highlanders. Before that I just thought of you as 'British soldiers'.

Looking back even after forty years the horror is still very real and clear. December 8th 1962 was a Saturday, and my father, Clifford Joseph, an air traffic controller at Anduki airfield was only supposed to work half a day.

He was supposed to come home to celebrate my birthday – the cake was baked and the chicken was cooking for dinner (the things one remembers) but of course he never did come home. Just before noon the rebels attacked Anduki airfield and captured all the Shell employees and contractors who were there. That evening my father, together with other hostages including Maurice Fern, Gus Kirby and Alistair Ker-Lindsay were bound, blindfolded, and used as human shields by the rebels who were trying to capture the Panaga Police Station. My father was killed in the gun battle that ensued.

My memories of that day are still very clear. I remember the sound of gunfire and my mother pulling mattresses off the beds and placing them over the glass windows. And I remember her shoving us kids under the bed and telling us that no matter what happened we had to stay hidden. My older brother was six, my second brother was four, I had just turned three and my sister was just a year old. My mother was four months pregnant with my youngest brother and I remember how calm she was in spite of everything going on around us. Our maid was wailing and wringing her hands and crying that we were all going to die and there was my mother trying to hold everything together for us.

I remember that first knock on the door and the wounded policeman who had ran from the Seria Police Station, bleeding from his side. Ours was certainly not the closest house and it saddens me to think that we were probably the only one to give him shelter. My mother, who had been a nurse, tended to his wound and then hid him in the attic.

It was late that evening when the second knock came to the door and it was two rebels who stood outside asking for food for my father. My mother packed everything we could spare and gave it to the rebels. We believe that my father was already dead by then but the rebels needed food. They were probably Shell employees who had joined the rebellion and they obviously knew that my father had been captured.

My mother wanted to get rid of them as quickly as she could because she was afraid that either the policeman would start shooting or that the rebels would search the house.

I don't remember anything else after that except the helicopter ride and, of course, you carrying me. I remember how terrified I was. My mother remembered you taking me from her as I was screaming (which was very unusual behaviour from me). I still have echoes in my mind of her yelling at me saying that you were trying to help me. That terrified child became an adult and was mortified at how she had behaved. Another soldier had grabbed my two brothers by the hand and was running with them towards the helicopter. We took nothing with us that day; we left with just the clothes on our backs.

My family and I have always been grateful to the soldiers of the Queen's Own Highlanders who came to the aid of Brunei. We know you were only doing your duty but you became our heroes and neither time nor distance will change that. And it is not often that one is given the opportunity to say 'Thank you' and I needed to do that.

Evelyn M. Campbell
Richmond Virginia USA

Chapter 1

The Long Journey

It was a cold snowbound day in February of 1994, as I disembarked the Caledonian night sleeper from Inverness. Euston was as busy as ever with commuters pushing and shoving, and I made my way to the Underground to catch the tube to Heathrow. I was travelling alone, with my old Burgin rucksack that last saw action some forty years ago in the Far East – bit tattered now, like me at the age of fifty-one. I was looking for that last big adventure that most old soldiers crave for. I had no plans, just memories, and I would just follow my instincts and see what happened. I had enough cash to survive on and plastic in reserve, and had purchased a twelve-month open air ticket from Singapore Airlines. I was free at last from a marriage that was doomed to failure. What had happened to all those in-between years of hard work as a Managing Director of my own business? What was it all for – to keep the lawyers, accountants and the tax man happy? Now I had dumped the lot and was heading for Singapore and the unknown.

At Heathrow I made my way to the self-service restaurant and went for the big breakfast. I found a table, with the remains of the last customer's meal spread all over it. Having finished my breakfast I left my mess on top of the clutter already there, now possibly for the next customer. The management seemed oblivious to the problem, or were they economising on cleaners?

I had plenty of time, so I made my way to the check-in desk of Singapore Airlines. I was browsing through books when I felt a tap on the shoulder and a voice said, "I recognise the old rucksack." I turned and was surprised to see Peter, another Jock, and old friend from my SAS days back in the sixties. "How are you doing, Jake? I had to look twice when I saw that old issue rucksack.

"Don't tell me you're off to the Far East too?"

"No, I'm going to South America – got a contract there – you should come, the pay's too good to miss."

"No thanks, Peter. I'm staying out of trouble this time. I remember the Congo – you said no trouble, then everyone found themselves running for their lives to Rhodesia and seeking asylum."

We went for a beer and sat and exchanged stories to fits of laughter. The time passed and soon it was time to exchange our farewells, and go our separate ways.

As soon as I entered the 747 of Singapore Airlines, I felt the weight of the world drop from my shoulders. I felt relaxed, as I was shown to my seat in Club Class by a very beautiful and charming Singapore girl. I stowed my gear in the overhead locker and settled in, watching business types struggle with suitcases that should have been in the cargo hold. Then I had to rise as a Singapore businessman, in a very smart silk suit, moved into the window seat next to me and we exchanged niceties. I could see the confused look on his face as he noted my mode of dress, and wondered why I was in Club Class, dressed in combat denim trousers, desert boots, black T-shirt and multi-pocket olive green fishing vest.

He started chatting away, telling me he was in book publishing and had been in London to do business with some publishing house. We were taxiing out to the runway when he suddenly went quiet as we prepared for take-off. While the engines increased to a roar and we were rolling, I watched as his hands turned white, gripping the seat rests as we were thrust back in our seats. He did not relax until we reached the top of our climb, when he took out his handkerchief and mopped his brow. Singapore girl appeared with hot towels, quickly followed by the meal menu and the drinks. I ordered a double brandy and a can of Tiger beer. My travelling companion ordered orange juice. We both ordered the same Asian dish of seafood – it was well served, and a pleasure to eat after Heathrow's attempt to feed the masses.

After the meal, I had another double brandy and Tiger, and settled back with my own thoughts. My companion was already working on his laptop. I finished my drinks and passed the empties to Singapore girl, and put my seat into the relax position. I closed my eyes and started to nod off, my thoughts drifting back to the last time I arrived in Singapore as a young soldier, on board the troop ship TT *Oxfordshire*. I was eighteen and the year was 1961.

Singapore looked marvellous as we entered the harbour; the sun was setting, with a red glow in the western sky. The harbour was bustling with junks and sampans going about their business. The air was pleasantly hot and smelt of spices and sweet smelling flowers. We disembarked and boarded our trucks for our various units: I was bound for Selarang Barracks at Changi to rejoin my unit – 1st Battalion, The Queen's Own Highlanders – after being left in the UK with the Rear Guard at Edinburgh Castle.

While the truck wound its way through the city streets of Singapore, I could see it was going to be a whole new way of life being here, as I took in the sights and smells – we weren't used to seeing so much activity: the hawker stalls cooking a thousand different delights, the bars, shops, and girls (this would be the scene every night)! Back home, there was nothing after 10.30 p.m. – maybe a fish supper on the way home from the pub and off to bed. It got me thinking that the UK was a third world country!

We arrived at Selarang Barracks, to be told we could not go out on our first night, so we went to the camp NAAFI bar for a few beers. It was then that I was reunited with my two old friends – Chalky and Sunshine.

Sunshine and I had enlisted at the age of fifteen as Infantry Junior Leaders back in 1958. I had known Chalky in Edinburgh, before our departure to Singapore. A Glasgow lad, stockily built with fair hair and blue eyes, he was always laughing and joking – a good soldier. Sunshine was from Edinburgh, with wiry build, red hair, spotty face and a grin whatever was happening, very tough and well trained.

"Well here we are together again – the experts in drinking, murder and arson," said Chalky, laughing.

We had a good chat about everything that had happened since we last met. Next morning we were up with the dawn and, by the time we had had breakfast and returned to our barrack room, the sun was climbing high in the sky – sweat was running down my back.

We were kitted up with our jungle greens and the rest of the gear we needed to fight in the jungle. Now it was the turn of the camp Medical Officer to frighten the hell out of us, as to the terrible diseases one can catch, for which the treatment was worse then the cause. Then we were issued with lists of all the 'out of bounds' areas in the city, such as the Hong Kong bar, Happy World, New World, Jungle Club and plenty more. It was clear to me that what had just been handed out was no more than a map of places for the Jocks to visit – save time finding them later.

Well, we were not to get the chance anyway, as we were transferred on to trucks for the journey north to Malaya, and the Jungle Warfare Training Centre where training would start in earnest. We hacked our way through miles of steaming jungle, sometimes up to our necks in swamps. I would watch as water spiders would run over the surface past my nose. Then one of us would get a foot caught on some roots or, worse, trip and go under. At the end of the day we would make camp for the night, and help each other burn off the leeches we had collected during the day. The night would come very quickly, about 1800 hours, and as it was pitch black, all one could do was to climb into a hammock under a poncho and sleep. Some nights there were terrible storms and the rains would last all night, with long flashes of lightning illuminating the surrounding area and throwing strange shadows everywhere. Trees could be heard crashing down, and bamboo would crack like a rifle shot putting one's nerves to the test.

We were the British contingent of the 99th Gurkha Infantry Brigade. Our main role was internal security, and aiding the police in preventing piracy. Our first operation was on the Thailand border looking for stray Chinese communists left over from the Fifties' emergencies.

We spent some time preparing to go to Vietnam as UN troops. Nam, as it was known, was just a small war at this time. The US only had military advisors there in 1961, to help train the South Vietnam Army. Fortunately for us, we were spared the Nam – the UK had other wars to fight.

To most people back home, Borneo is just a name on a map. Ask them to point it out, and very few can! I know it exists: I was there in the flare of my youth as a young soldier – we were the first since the Japanese surrendered at the end of WW2, some fifteen years before.

We were patrolling eastwards along the northern coast of Borneo on board HMS *Puncheston*, one of three minesweepers, with five Jocks on each to act as marines. We rounded the top of Borneo, and turned south with the Philippines on the horizon to the east. This area was known to be rife with pirates, and good hunting was to be had. These pirates had been in this game for generations and were very experienced, bloodthirsty killers, who had no mercy on their victims; much like the Vikings around the coasts of Europe way back.

But this was 1961, and to people back home this sort of thing was 'unbelievable in this day and age'. Even today, people still laugh when pirates come up in conversation – but then they weren't there!

In an area known as Darvel Bay near Sandakan one of the Jocks up in the lookout spotted a pirate vessel – a junk with at least four large outboards – take off at high speed towards the coastline of mangrove swamps. We followed at a much slower speed with the foredeck gun sending shell after shell in their direction until they disappeared into the mangrove. We had to stop about one mile short of the coast and lower our inflatable with outboard. Five Jocks and one sailor clambered on board and headed for the swamp, and as we entered, the mangrove closed in around us, forcing us to slow to a crawl, senses very alert now.

It was hot and humid and smelt of decaying vegetation; sweat was running as we scanned the way ahead. It was clear which way the junk had gone by the disturbed muddy water, which still lingered after their passage. Suddenly we spotted the vessel just one hundred yards ahead. We stopped to look through the binoculars – no movement spotted, no sound heard. Two of the lads started to paddle.

The jungle had become very still, as if something was about to happen. Our fingers sweating on the triggers, I said, "Ahead slowly." As we got closer I could see that the outboards had gone, but still no noise. They could not be far ahead if they were on foot. We came alongside and I climbed aboard with my cover man. It looked deserted. My finger was sweating on the trigger, the safety switch off, but they had taken everything they could carry. This mooring had been used before, as there was a three-plank wide jetty the vessel was tied up to. At the end of the jetty, a plank walkway disappeared into the jungle.

On board the junk, we found the hatchway was booby-trapped – wired to a grenade, sitting on what looked like a drum of fuel. We left it alone and climbed back onto our own craft. I briefed the others, and we decided to torch the bugger.

I lit a packet of hexamine solid fuel cooking tablets, and chucked it on board amongst some rubbish. "Let's get out of here, sailor!"

We backed off slowly, watching the surrounding jungle. I was expecting a shot to ring out at any moment, as I felt someone was watching us. "I think they're very close as they didn't have time to get far with all that gear," I said.

We could see a few flames now, and plenty of smoke. Then the explosion came as the booby trap went off. Suddenly the jungle was alive again, as if it had been holding its breath. Monkeys screeched and the air was filled with fruit bats; crocodiles could be seen around us. We were soon out of sight and glad to be back on the open sea again. We boarded HMS *Puncheston* and reported to the Captain, who was pleased to see us back, after hearing all the commotion. We left the area and sailed into Sandakan for two nights ashore, to sample the local delights. Now it was time for us Jocks to say goodbye to the Royal Navy, and rejoin the rest of 'A' Company in Tawau South East Sabah (very close to the Indonesian border).

Eventually we returned to sea, with the local police patrol boats (thirty foot vessels with a single engine, very cramped, and the loo over the back end!). This time I had an eight man patrol plus three police officers. I was starting to think I was in the Navy not the Army!

The next patrol was quite unreal. As we approached a remote island, we saw men standing on the jetty. Drawing nearer I could see about fifteen, some dressed partly in Japanese uniform with lace-up caps. All were bowing as we came alongside. "What's going on here?" I asked the police.

"They are Japanese soldiers. You are the first military they have seen since the war, and they are afraid. The war passed them by and they turned to fishing, and have lived here for sixteen years; the mainland was not safe for them, as the head hunters have killed all the Japanese military – thousands of them – and collected their weapons along with their heads."

"Where are their weapons?" I asked.

"They say they have no weapons," was the reply.

Once they realised we meant no harm, they came forward with information about pirates, and told how they had to hide from them. If I was in their position, I would most certainly have kept my weapons close at hand. How else could they defend themselves? We packed up and left, as we did not like the thought of sleeping on this island.

Two days' sailing brought us to another island, surrounded by coral, but we found a way in and beached. This looked like a good place to camp. The island was no more than a mile long by half a mile wide – golden sands, palm trees, with some jungle in the centre. I went off with one of the lads for a look around while the rest of the men unloaded the kit. I was looking for fresh water, or any fruit and wild pigs which frequented these islands. Although we were not expecting anyone to be on this island, I became aware of meat cooking – and our senses pricked up.

"You go back and tell the others to get up here fast with one of the police. Tell the remainder to stay at the boat. I'll be at that tree over there." He scurried off and was back soon with the lads.

"Let's go find out what's cooking." We slowly moved forward, and were just about to emerge from the bush, having reached the far side of the island, when we heard a voice. We froze and went to ground. The lads crawled up into an extended line. What we saw we could not fully comprehend; there were eight pirates – most of them sitting around a fire. A big chunk of meat was hanging from a tree branch over a fire; their boat was bow into the beach.

"OK, lads, let's advance in extended line and see what happens. They could just be fishermen for all we know!"

We stood up and started to advance. It was now late afternoon, and the night would not be long in coming. We advanced out of the dark shadows, the pirates being silhouetted by the setting sun. We had covered more than one hundred yards – and still had another two hundred to go, when the alarm went up, and the first shots, definitely not friendly, came in our direction. We went to ground and returned the fire. Five of the pirates reached the boat and attempted to push it out to sea, but we ran forward firing and shouting our heads off, as the last three pirates fell dead in the waves. We gathered around the scene to view the carnage: bodies, firearms, personal kit, and the sea red with blood. Then we noticed the meat still hanging over the fire. That was when the full horror hit us. It was barely recognisable, but it was a man! These bastards were cannibalising some poor sod; large slices of arms and legs were already gone, and the head was sitting next to the fire on a log, nose and ears missing – what a mess.

There was nothing of importance on the boat, so we took photos and handprints of the dead for the police. We then piled the bodies and head onto the boat, along with the meat. Gas oil was poured over everything and set on fire. We watched as it drifted out to sea like a Viking funeral then made our way back to our patrol boat. That night we decided to sleep on board – one hundred yards offshore with a double guard posted. We had no intention of ending up as burgers for pirates!

After returning to our base area in Tawau, information was received from the police that pirates were operating from the island of Sebatik, just a few miles opposite Tawau. The pirates had been on a raid off a coastal village, some miles up the coast, and were spotted and tracked by local fishermen, who reported to the police. The job now fell to us to go in after them. We didn't expect to find any sign of the pirates, as they were not going to hang around, but would blend into the surrounding communities if there were any.

Information was very sketchy, as this island was divided by the Indonesian border, and nothing was known about what was on the other side.

We set off at first light in three small rowboats, fitted with outboards. The crossing did not take long, but when we beached we were in thick, waist-deep mud. By the time we reached dry land, we were grey from head to foot, making us took somewhat ghost-like as the mud started to dry.

The pirates would feel safe here as no one in their right minds would attempt to land here except the Brits. We continued scouting the area all morning, with no sign of life.

Just as we were about to give up, we suddenly came face to face with pirates armed with shotguns and old rifles. Time stood still as we faced each other. Then the pirates, seeing the weapons pointing in their direction, dropped their guns and we lowered ours. Our patrol Police Officer asked if they were pirates. The leader spoke English and said they were smugglers, and would give us half of what they had if we made no trouble. The Corporal in charge of this patrol was all for this, so the smugglers split up cartons of cigarettes – half to the Jocks, half for the home team.

"See, we friends now, no need to fight," said the leader. They then indicated to us to follow for a drink at their village. We all picked up our guns and followed them into the village, but I did not like the way things were developing. You could not call it a village – just five buildings constructed of bamboo and rattan. There was a clear area in the middle of the village with a volleyball net across it. I was getting somewhat apprehensive, my eyes looking for trouble.

What were these little bastards up to? Why was the patrol Corporal falling for this? I smelt trouble. We entered the largest building and were surprised to see it was used as a clubhouse with a bar. This was not right, with just four other huts around – no women, no children. We were offered ice-cold Anchor beer, and the Jocks jumped at it. In this heat it was welcome.

Then there came another surprise as one of the two men behind the bar said, in perfect English, "We don't want any trouble – we do some business, you can drink all you want, we all friends, yes?"

There was no hesitation as the Jocks accepted the offer, especially with the fact we had no Officers with us. But I did not trust this lot, and felt we were being sucked in for a slapping. I approached the Corporal and made the suggestion that we send a report to base of our location and this village. He was not concerned about the situation as he emptied his first can of beer, and opened his second. He gave me our position and I was told to send it.

Sending a signal was not as easy it sounds, as this had to go out in Morse code, and an antenna had to be erected up in the tree line. The signaller and I got to work, watched by two of our new found friends. Eventually we sent our signal and awaited the reply.

Half an hour passed, and I went over to the main hut. The lads were well pissed by now. I knew it only took two beers to get the locals pissed. If they thought they were going to get the Jocks drunk that easily then give them a slapping, they had better think again!

I got two beers and returned to the signaller, who had a reply from base which read:

"*Get out of there now. You are five miles inside Indonesian territory.*"

"Shit! Get this antenna down now, pal. I hope there are no Indo troops in the area."

"Jake! The two that were watching us have gone." I left the signaller to it as I made my way to the rest of the lads, and passed the message to the well-pissed Corporal. By this time, the lads were fighting among themselves, busting chairs over each other and helping themselves to the bar.

"For Christ's sake, Corporal, let's move. I think all our friends have fled – maybe Indo troops on the way." That got his attention – then I noticed the flicker of flames at the back of the building, spreading fast. Somehow everyone was outside again in the blinding sun, struggling into their equipment and running back the way we had come into the village.

We ran to put as much distance as we could between us and the village, before collapsing into sweating heaps on the jungle floor, automatically taking up all-around defence and a quick check to make sure no one had been left behind. With the alcohol pumping out of the skin, the lads sobered up and struggled to their feet, continuing our forced march back to the boats. We climbed aboard from the stinking, sucking mud – totally exhausted, but once again very lucky we had come through this without loss.

When we arrived at base, the Corporal reported to the Company Commander for a ticking-off for crossing the border, but nothing was said about what really happened. As far as the Jocks were concerned, they had plenty of fags to last for a while and had had a good laugh into the bargain.

The Battalion boards HMS Bulwark *for exercise on East coast Malay 1962*

Wessex helicopters ready for deployment

*Pte R. Munro and stick
ready to board*

Malaya 1961

Lt. J.J. MacKenzie and members of 1and 2 Platoons Malaya 1961

February 1962.
Five Q.O. Highlanders join HMS Puncheston *on Anti Piracy Patrols*

Refuelling at sea

Middle: Bill Strang
Right: Rab Dall

Stokers mess rum rations

Sgt Gosgrove demonstrates the SLR
to ships Captain

Bill Strang up in the crows nest

Rest in Kuching

Local Police pay a visit

Safe return to Singapore after many weeks at sea
including a typhoon lasting three days

The author on anti-piracy patrol March 1962
on Tawau Police Boat P5

1 Sect. A. Coy on board Police Patrol boat 5 Tawau apprehend pirates

Two pirates squat while awaiting police transport
protected from locals by 1 Sect

Chapter 2

Lion City

Back in Singapore we were given some time to ourselves – a little R&R you could say. One Friday night, Sunshine, Chalky and I decided to have a night out downtown. We took a taxi to the Happy World and then on to the Hong Kong bar. When we entered, we found the place was wall to wall military uniforms – Navy, Army and Air Force – every man and his dog was there – who cared if it was out of bounds? We fought our way through the smoke and cheap perfume towards the bar. Girls were dancing on the tables, stripping to loud rock music coming from a juke box in a corner somewhere.

"This looks like the place for us!" said Chalky in his strong Glasgow accent. We pushed our way to the bar, shouting above the din for pints of Tiger. We held our ground at the bar – the first two pints went down well and we got in the third round. We noticed the bar girls were doing a roaring trade, taking customers up the stairs at the far side of the bar, and it was not long before they would return for the next customer. The girls were straight to the point –

"You want short time, John? Ten dollar short time, twenty all night. You buy me drink?" We had just settled into our new surroundings when all hell was to be let loose. The Military Police were pouring through the front door, whistles blowing and batons swinging.

"Time to get out lads!" We made for the back stairs, Sunshine leading the way. The place was already like some Wild West movie – girls screaming, chairs flying, the sound of glass breaking. I was halfway to the stairs when I went down with a blow across my back from a baton that nearly bust my right arm. The MP bent down to grab me, trying to yank me to my feet as Chalky, who was behind me, turned and picked up a bottle, and smashed the MP across the face below the helmet line breaking the bottle. I scrambled to my feet and the three of us made it up the stairs with MPs in hot pursuit. On the landing we found the juke box that was still blasting out an Elvis number. We took hold of it and pushed it down the stairs, catching two MPs, throwing them back to the ground floor (the two now screaming with pain). We ran along the corridor looking for a way out. Doors opened, girls and clients appeared, asking, "What's going on?"

"MPs' raid!" we shouted, then there was a scramble.

A girl said, "Follow me this way out." We followed the girl into a room. She went to the window and started to open it, as we became aware of a sailor who had unfinished business with a ladyboy in the room. He was not amused to see us and voiced his anger.

Chalky shouted at him, "One in the bum no harm done!" We dropped from the window onto a tin roof and then to the yard below, legged it up a dark alley and then on to a main street, and disappeared into the masses. It was now after midnight as we found a taxi to Bugis Street, still laughing our nuts off.

We decided it was time to eat, and picked a hawker stall that was busy with locals, always a good sign. We ordered roast chicken and chips, and three ice cold pints of Tiger, then sat back to watch the scene: prostitutes on one side of the street, and ladyboys working the other. They looked sexier than the women, and were doing better business with the visiting Navy. We watched as sailor after sailor walked off with a ladyboy – the girls took second place. We, being based locally, knew the score as this was the basis of talk around camp, but I must say it was amusing.

As we got stuck into our chicken and chips and Tiger beer – very good it was too, even at two in the morning – I noticed a young Indian man – he looked in his twenties – enter the public toilets. As he re-emerged a gang of Chinese youths stabbed him and ran off. No one moved as the man slid down the wall and died – we carried on eating. A policeman walked over to the body and gave it a kick twice to see if he was dead, then went off for help.

"Just like Glasgow on Saturday night," said Chalky.

We left the scene and went to another bar and sat outside under a canvas lean-to, with a strip light on the wall – the small chit-chat lizards munching on any insects that came near the light. We bought a beer each and chatted over the night's events to roars of laughter. We had only been there for ten minutes when two Land-Rovers pulled up and out emerged eight MPs. We thought they were after us at first, for the earlier rammy, but they ran through a door ten feet to our right – it was a brothel raid.

"Let's drink up and go," said Sunshine.

Then the overhead canvas burst and a sailor landed on our table dressed in underpants with his sailor suit tucked under his arm. The table turned over along with our drinks. We were on our feet and running from the scene along with the sailor, who I now recognised from back home. We rounded a corner and stopped as our new found friend got dressed. "Nicky, what the hell are you doing here?"

"Nice to see you to Jake: shit I need a drink".

"You can buy us a round for spilling ours," said Sunshine.

So we took a taxi to the Brit Club, to find it was closed, but soon found a bar nearby and got a round in. Nicky told us he was a stoker on board HMS *Hermes* now. Then Chalky added, "What were you stoking in that place of ill repute?"

"She was all right, a real cracker," said Nicky.

"Got the pox more like," said Sunshine. "Maybe it was a boy? You best go and see the Medical Officer when you get back to HMS *Herpes*, you mangy sod!" We all laughed.

"Listen, we had best get back to camp before anything else happens. When you're next in Singapore give us a call at the camp and we'll have a night out."

We stopped a taxi for Nicky and he vanished as quickly as he had appeared. We found a taxi to take us back to camp but, as we were passing Bugis Street, we saw two sailors running past us with a gang of Chinese after them. The sailors turned and tried to run back through the gang, but were pulled to the ground. I shouted to the taxi driver to "Get us out of here", and he pulled away quickly, but not before we witnessed a young Chinese man break a bottle and cut the sailor's throat. The other sailor was sitting propped up against a wall, bleeding badly. The same policeman we had seen kick the Indian boy's body was also witness to the proceedings and once again did not interfere.

These sailors had probably got into an argument over payment for something – refused to pay and now the poor sods were dead. It had been one hell of a Friday night and we would sleep well on it and most of Saturday!

The next afternoon I went into Changi village by myself to do some shopping and to find something to eat. I walked around for a while to get the last night's happenings out of my system, then I sat outside a bar next to an old Indian man working his hawker stall, making curry and chapattis; I ordered curry and a pint of Tiger from the bar. A Chinese girl appeared with my drink and sat down beside me, as my curry arrived from the next vendor. The Chinese girl was looking me over. I noticed her eyes on the Gurkha knife arm flashes on my jungle shirt.

She was a stunner – about five foot five, skinny by western standards but had a very nicely shaped body, long neck, high cheek bones and devilish smile. Her hair was done up into a beehive style, with a long ponytail half way down her back. She was wearing a tight-fitting, long blue Chinese dress, which did credit to her figure.

"You up at Camp Selarang?"

"Yes," I replied.

"You here Singapore long time?"

"No."

"You buy me drink?

"OK," anything for peace while I ate, and off she went and returned with some green concoction and sat down.

"Would you like to eat?" I asked.

"No thank you, I have eaten already. My name is Susie, what are you called?" she asked before I could introduce myself.

"Jake, they call me Jake. Nickname: 'Jake Two Knife'."

"I like you."

"I like you too. You live here?"

"Not so far by taxi. Downtown Singapore," she replied. She did most of the talking and seemed to want a lot of information about me that I was not about to tell, so I bluffed my way and listened to what she was saying. This was not the usual chat-up by a local girl. There was something sinister about the line of questions, however I was still interested, and wanted to know more about this girl.

"What are you doing tonight?" I asked.

"Wash hair and go to my father's house."

"How about next Saturday?"

"OK, OK."

We made a date and I departed, still puzzled at the line of questions but not really expecting to see her again.

The week seemed to drag on and on, but I could not get her and the questions out of my head. I met Chalky and Sunshine most nights in the NAAFI bar, but said nothing of Susie.

Saturday arrived, and I went downtown dressed in a white shirt and black trousers, not telling the others I was going out. I was pleasantly surprised to see Susie at the entrance to the Orchard Hotel – I hadn't expected her to turn up.

She was looking stunning, in a cream silk trouser suit, hair and make-up done to perfection. I complimented her, and she returned it with a smile. We went to the movies and then for a meal at a little place down by the river.

It was strange, no questions were being asked. Was it just my imagination? "Forget it," I thought. The night was progressing and we really had enjoyed each other's company – well I certainly had. Then she said, "You want to stay my place tonight?" I jumped at the offer.

"Yes, that sounds good to me."

"We go," she said, and put out her hand for a taxi. A yellow car stopped, we got in and settled down. I noticed the vehicle had no meter, but that in itself wasn't unusual in Singapore. She was chatting away in Chinese to the driver, and I was wondering where we were going to end up, when we swung into a dark driveway between two high stone pillars with dragons on top. Then a large colonial house appeared out of the gloom.

"Shit, what have I got into now?" was the first thing to go through my head as we pulled up at the door.

The door was arched, with oil-filled coach lights flickering shadows around the doorway. A doorman dressed in a black suit and bow tie stepped forward and opened the cab door. Susie climbed out, followed by myself. I was growing increasingly nervous as we entered a very large reception area, with a chandelier ten feet across. There were two suits of Chinese armour standing on a very highly polished marble floor. I counted eight doors leading off, and a staircase that was straight out of a Hollywood movie. One door opened and a girl dressed to the nines looked out as if to see who had just arrived. She made a greeting to Susie, then popped back into the room and shut the door – not before I heard laughing and high sprits from inside the room full of people. Susie was heading for the stairs.

"What's going on in there?" I asked.

"Friends, doing a little gambling," she replied, putting a finger to her red lips indicating me to keep quiet.

On the upper landing there were more suits of Chinese armour and about a dozen doors. The lighting was low and the ceiling fans hummed away but did not hide the sound of Chinese music coming from somewhere. Susie pulled a key from her handbag and opened a door. We entered, and my first thoughts were, "Bloody hell, I'm in heaven!"

The room was enormous, and the most luxurious I had ever seen – the painted ceiling, the chandelier, the silk curtains – the bed was big enough for six and even the bedding was silk.

"Susie, what is this place – what's going on – I can't afford a night here." It was my turn to ask questions. She put her handbag on the dressing table and turned to approach me with her arms outstretched to go round my neck.

"You not happy here? I make you happy. This is my father's house," she said.

"How can your father afford all this? I've never seen a place like it. I thought maybe you had a flat someplace. What were you doing at the bar in Changi village?"

"Questions, questions," she said.

"What do you expect?" I answered.

"I answer your question in the bath," she said, starting to strip.

"Christ!" I was starting to get excited now. I got out of my clothes and entered the bathroom. She was already in the water. The bath (big enough for my whole squad) was sunk into the floor and tiled with Chinese lions and dragons. The water was hot, oiled, and smelt like heaven to me. I started to relax: in for a penny in for a pound – what the hell?

Her arms suddenly came round my neck, and our lips met, then we made love. It was fantastic. Later, we crawled out of the bath exhausted, dried off and jumped on the bed. Susie chucked a bathrobe in my direction. She poured brandy and soda into crystal glasses and handed me one.

"I make you happy, yes?"

"Yes you do, but why me? You could have anyone you fancy."

She was drying her hair with a towel as she turned to me, "Yes, I can have what I want – and I want you. You're my all-time boyfriend from now on – OK?"

"OK!" I replied. She joined me on the bed and we talked, made love, talked some more and slept like babies.

I awoke wondering if I was dreaming and would find myself in an army issue bed, complete with blood sucking bed bugs as was the norm. As my eyes grew used to the bright sunlight coming in from the balcony, I saw her sitting relaxed at a table, her long hair shining black in the morning sun. She was quite stunning.

"Good morning, Jake. Come and eat some breakfast." I put on the robe and went over and kissed her on the forehead as she squeezed my hand. I sat down in front of a display of watermelon, papaya, pineapple, rice, fish, and soup.

"Have you just cooked this?"

"No," she laughed, "I asked the house staff to send it up. You like?"

"You ever try army rations? Well, now, what are we going to do for the rest of the day, Susie?"

"We make love all day?"

"OK with me!" I ate my fill and then asked about her father.

"My father is government official – works with Customs Department. He owns many bars, gambling clubs and hotels, here and in Malaya – and some smuggling operations we call 'monkey business'. The day I meet you I was visiting one of my father's bars to collect money, when I saw you and took your order."

"The lads back at camp won't believe this!"

"Do not tell anyone, it is safer that way for all," she said.

"Is your father here now? Will he be angry?"

"No, he is in Hong Kong on business. When he is away, I and my sister run things here – I do what I like. I don't see him much; he has other women here and there. My mother died just after we were five years old, so the house staff looked after us and are very loyal."

"What about all the rooms here?"

"Mostly bar and club girls – earn plenty money, bring customers here every night. We also rent rooms for private parties – big money. Come, I show you." Susie crossed the room and opened what I thought was a cupboard. We entered a room about ten feet by six. There was a single low watt bulb hanging from the ceiling with no shade; a desk with a TV set and some kind of control panel; a telephone, and a radio transmitter of British origin still in army green. I had not seen a TV since I left the UK.

"Probably Coronation Street is on!"

"What is this Coronation Street?" asked Susie.

"Oh, just a UK TV programme."

"No TV in Singapore, coming soon I think." Susie turned on the TV and the screen slowly lit up. She messed around with the control system, and I could not believe my eyes as the scene changed from one room to another. She stopped at a scene of a man in bed with two girls, all asleep.

"This man is very important. He is in Russian Embassy, and he spends much time and money here. We have photos of his actions we keep for a rainy day, as the English say."

"You have a wicked mind, Susie."

She laughed. "This is business." The picture changed, and another man and women zoomed into view. "Western business man, he comes here every time he is in Singapore. How much you make in one week, Jake?"

"£1 a day UK, that's $75 dollars a week Singapore," I replied.

"How would like $5,000.00 for one night's work?"

"Are you kidding? That's a fortune to the likes of me. Is this why I am here?" I asked.

"No, Jake. But why not get your share? I'm offering you a chance here. You are not going to make money in the army – maybe get killed – for what, and who cares anyway?"

"What do you want me to do?"

"I have inside information about Flagstaff House." My ears pricked up with dread. "The next time you are on guard there, let me know and I will tell you more. There is no danger in this for you."

"If you trust me tell me now."

"OK," she said. "There are certain documents in the office and we want to photo them. All you have to do is get on the midnight patrol. We know the patrols are of two soldiers at a time for two hours. At 0015 hours you should be passing the house on the downhill towards the guardroom, and not return to the house for thirty-two minutes approximately. That is all that is required. We do the rest and you get $5,000.00 – half before and the rest on completion." So this is why she was eyeing up my unit insignia back at Changi village last week. She was well informed as to our duties.

"You really have done your homework, Susie. Would this have anything to do with that Russian embassy man?"

"No, Jake. This is only for future of Singapore when we get independence."

"OK, I will do it."

"See I make you happy. Tell no one. Together we make money, yes?"

"Yes, let's do it," I said grinning. "You do realise if I get caught I'll be shot at dawn?"

"You maybe get shot anyway, Jake. This way you make money, and you will not be in the army forever."

"Good point Susie."

"Why they call you 'Jake Two Knife'?"

"Because I carry two knives, which gave me the nickname." I went over to my jacket and removed the Javanese double-edged throwing knife for Susie to inspect. These were handed down to me from a uncle who was in Java a long time ago, and I have spent many long hours learning the skill of throwing.

"Let's change the subject and go to the beach for the rest of the day." We got ready and left for the beach up near Changi point. We had a good day's swimming, but it was soon time for me to return to camp, so we walked into Changi and found a taxi. As we had to pass Selarang Barracks on the way, I was dropped near the front gate. I said my farewells to Susie and watched as the taxi sped off in the direction of Singapore.

Chapter 3

Uncertain Times

Returning to camp was hell after the luxury I'd had for the last weekend. This was going to be a real nightmare.

Should I tell someone of the events and the planned break-in? I had no proof, and if I told my platoon Sergeant he would go running to the company Sergeant Major, and I would be in a world of shit and confined to camp for a month while the Special Branch investigated. If they found nothing then I would get 'jail time' for wasting everyone's time. I wasn't in the habit of drawing attention to myself, and I certainly didn't want to be confined to camp after what I had just experienced.

Sunshine came into the billet and approached me as I sat on my bed, deep in thought.

"What's going down, Jake? I haven't seen you since last Friday night. What's up?"

"Nothing – well nothing you would believe."

"Try me. I know you of old, and there's something going down."

Chalky arrived and joined in.

"Pissed off without us on Friday – not a word. You're up to something China, I can smell it." So I told the story – all except the break-in. The two of them sat there on my bed beaming.

"Bloody hell you lucky sod!" said Sunshine.

"Well stuff me with little green apples!" said Chalky.

"What do you think I should do, fellers?"

The reply came from a grinning Chalky. "Better see the Medical Officer." I looked at them both and then we all laughed. I'd never given that a thought.

Then it was my time for guard duty at Flagstaff House. I was going to be on twenty-four hours next weekend; now all I had to do was manipulate the hours so I was on 'midnight to two a.m.', and no problems.

I spent a night with Susie, and she was pleased and quite excited about it all. "I hope all goes well and your friends don't get caught. Even in the grounds, I can't be responsible if they are seen and shot. Have you thought about visitors, parties and functions?"

"The staff there keep us informed: no one at home this weekend. If there are any changes we will know. Jake, put this in your bank account." Susie handed me an envelope stuffed with $50 dollar bills.

"I don't have a bank account."

"We soon change that. Come on," said Susie, and off we went to a bank downtown where Susie seemed to be well known. I opened an account, deposited the money, and was given a passbook that would have to stay with Susie as I could not risk being caught with it in camp. "Come – I have rounds to do collecting money from my father's businesses. You can come with me."

When we came out of the bank, there was a yellow car waiting for us. As we climbed in, I recognised the driver – yes, it was the same car we were in the first night. There was a briefcase on the back seat, which Susie picked up and placed on her lap.

I started to take note of the driver, who wore a black suit and tie. As I looked into his driving mirror, I could see the butt of an automatic handgun sticking out of his shoulder holster. Susie introduced us.

"Jake, this is Tang. He works for my father and he speaks a little English, don't you Tang?"

"Hi, Mister Jake, I look out for you now."

"Thank you, Tang," I replied. I was thinking I'd look after myself with this lot!

We arrived outside a shop in Anson Road. It looked like a general store, with pots, pans and oil lamps hanging outside. Susie went in and I followed, while Tang stayed in the car. The proprietor was an old Chinese man, with his wife standing beside him. They both looked nervous, and their eyes darted between Susie and me. A packet was handed to Susie. She opened it, counted the money, put it into the briefcase, then turned and left without as much as a thank you or goodbye. I followed her back out to the car.

"Protection money," she said, smiling. "We give good protection. But there are too many gangs operating here, and sometimes there is trouble."

We did the rounds, and what I saw was an eye-opener. Shit, I must have led a sheltered life up to now! Going round the shops was OK, but the gambling dens and brothels were something else, as they are run by smaller gangs and could change sides at anytime.

When we arrived at the first of these, Susie was joined by four more of Daddy's boys all dressed in black suits and tooled up.

I felt quite naked with my two knives, yet I was quite honoured to be accepted and see what went on in a gang like this. I started to think I could be getting into something here – why was I being allowed to see all this, was there more to this than Susie and money? I followed Susie and the rest of the gang, staying well in the background while the deals were done. The collections made, we returned to Daddy's house.

As we turned into the driveway Susie said, "That's my sister at the door with doorman." We pulled up and got out. "Jake this is my sister Mai Ling."

"Hi Jake, you welcome here." Another surprise – I could not tell them apart.

"You're twins!" I said.

"Oh, yes," said Mai Ling.

We entered a room and the minders stayed in the hall. The door closed, and I turned as I heard the security locks drop into place. The girls were emptying the contents of two briefcases on a very highly polished table that had a large shaded light hanging low in the centre. The rest of the room was in darkness. It was clear to me that Mai Ling had also been 'doing the rounds'.

A panel in the wall opened, with a burst of light from another room. Two men entered, dressed in black suits and ties. The panel closed and once again we were in the dark. They came in my direction, putting out their hands to shake mine and greet me. Neither spoke English, so Susie did the honours. "It's OK, Jake. They know all about you, no problem."

The two sat down at the table and started to count faster than machine guns. I had only seen so much cash in my dreams, and it was staggering.

"Come, Jake. We go and eat," said Mai Ling, leading the way to a dining room that made the officers' mess look like the Salvation Army.

The room was wood-panelled, with dozens of paintings, statuettes, silver candlesticks, and very large wooden bowls piled high with fruits of kinds I had never seen before. At the far end of the room there was a large gold Buddha with incense sticks burning, giving off a sweet aroma. One end of the table was laid for three. The kitchen staff appeared with trays of food and laid them in front of us – we dined well. I still couldn't get over these two lookalikes.

How was I going to tell them apart? I needed some sign or signal between Susie and myself. The three of us chatted about the day's work then I brought up the subject of security.

"Ah," said the two girls together, "we were waiting to see if you would bring up that subject." Now I'd walked right into shit. "Jake, I have been watching you make observations and we need your help. You are army and see things we do not, and we see things you do not. Therefore, if we put our heads together, we can do better. Sometimes things happen – other gangs muscle in and cause trouble when we collect."

"I'll work on it for you."

"We look after you well, Jake," said Mai Ling.

"You already do," I replied.

"Jake, about the other business, I have more information now. Our people will get into Flagstaff House by the kitchen door. This has been arranged by the housekeeper, who will not be harmed. Nothing will be taken, only photographs of documents and then they'll be out of there. No one will ever now."

"Sounds ninety-nine point nine percent perfect to me."

The two girls looked at me and Susie said, "Jake, we miss something?"

"No, you have planned this as well as could be, but there is always the unlikely event of the unpredictable happening."

"We understand now your thinking – good, very good."

"Saturday is 'go' then. I'll see you on Sunday, ladies. I must return to camp as I have many boring things to do to get ready for this guard."

"OK, Jake, I get one of our drivers to take you back to camp." I walked to the front door, one girl on each arm, and kissed them both as I was getting into the car – I still couldn't tell them apart, and was still thinking 'Why do they need me?'

Chapter 4

Flagstaff House

Saturday – we paraded for guard duty at Flagstaff House in our kilts and white tunics, looking very smart, but very uncomfortable in the morning heat, with sweat running down one's legs and splashing off one's spats. The piper played and the duty officer inspected the guard. There were crowds of locals watching, as they do everywhere when there is a parade. Then, to my surprise, I saw Susie and Mai Ling – or was it Mai Ling and Susie? The girls must have come to double-check that I was on guard – good girls. We started to march off to the guardroom, thank God. After dark we changed into our greens and jungle boots, with twenty rounds of 7.62 and fixed bayonets. I went out with my cover man, a friend called Raggie, at midnight. I led on the right side of the roadway and he followed ten paces behind, covering my rear on the left. We rounded the house at 0015 hours. It was in darkness and I saw nothing.

"Shall we check the doors and windows, Jake?"

"No, we can do that on our next pass, Raggie." We headed back onto the roadway, which looped back to the guardroom. We got halfway when Raggie said, "I'm going to have a fag." I stopped, and we closed up for a rest. "What's up, Jake?"

"Nothing, just listen – traffic and the crickets, pal!"

"Funny how you don't hear it till you stop and listen."

"That's because we get used to it."

"Anyone could come in here. We'd never hear them with this racket."

"Don't think we'd see much with all this shrubbery about, until someone steps out and we stick them with the bayonet!"

"Let's move on," I said, and we continued our patrol and saw nothing.

On our next circuit, we checked all doors and windows and entered it on the guardroom report. The next day we changed guard and returned to camp. I had to wait till Friday before I could next leave camp. It was a long week. Sunshine and Chalky sat down beside me in the cookhouse, and Sunshine said, "We going out this weekend?"

"No, not this week, I've something on?"

"At it again," said Chalky.

"It'll come off in your hand one day. She got any sisters, Jake?"

"Yes, she's a twin – I can't tell them apart."

"Done both of them?"

"No, I have not!"

"How do you know?" he said, grinning from ear to ear.

"How about fixing us up?"

"I can't fix you up just like that. It's a bit tricky at the moment but I will give it some consideration – for a fee for old friends."

"Piss off, Jake!"

"Here you two, stick this in your pocket."

"Fifty bucks! What you up to, Jake?"

"Don't ask – just enjoy it, and keep it to yourself." I got up and left, but they both followed me.

"Jake, we're worried about you. You must be up to your neck in it again – we can see that. Let us in, man. Let us cover your rear in case you need help."

"Let me think about it. That might be a good idea."

I was out the gate fast after duties, midday of December 6th, 1962. I took a taxi into Singapore and met Susie at the usual place in front of the Orchard Hotel. We had agreed it was too dangerous for me to be seen going to and from her father's house in a taxi alone. She was looking marvellous in a tight-fitting, black Chinese dress. After all the niceties were over, I asked

"Did all go well?"

She looked me in the eye and smiled. "You bet it did, Jake – me, very happy." I would have liked to know how much she got, but was happy with my cut, so best not to ask and upset things. "Let's go to the movies, Jake. I want to see Gone with the Wind."

"Is that about a fat man who ate too much curry?" I asked.

She laughed and laughed. "You crazy man, Jake, but I love you."

She enjoyed the film, and had to go fix her make-up halfway through. I just wanted to get her home and into bed, but she wanted to eat. So we went to Bugis Junction of all places – very much a red light district, but good food could be had into the small hours of the morning.

We drew a lot of attention from service personal and families. If I was going to run into someone I knew then this was the place. Well, we had just sat down and ordered our meal when I got a tap on the shoulder. I turned to see Sunshine and Chalky grinning at me. "Oh, shit!" was my first thought.

"Hi, boys, want a beer? Susie, these are my best friends – Sunshine and Chalky."

"Hi, boys, please join us. Would you like a beer and something to eat?"

Both joined us, pulling up a chair each and shouting for attention from the hawker boys waiting to take their orders.

"Well boys, you no girlfriends in Singapore?" asked Susie.

"We thought you might help us out," said Chalky. The beers arrived and the food right behind.

Then Susie said, "I fix you two up with girls for tonight." That was fine with the lads. "Don't worry about cost: I will pay for your meal and the girls' time."

After the meal, and a few more beers, we walked to the end of the street and there was Tang sitting in the yellow car waiting for us. Susie had not said a word about this arrangement, but I was getting used to the unexpected. Susie and I climbed into the front with Tang, and the other two went in the back. Susie turned to me and said, "You have good friends, I like them. You tell them about us?"

"No, but they know I have girlfriend in town."

"OK, I fix it for them. I know lots of nice girls."

"I bet you do!" I thought.

Susie gave instructions to Tang and we changed direction, and soon came to a dark street with no street lights – only lights over front doors. We turned up a drive and stopped in front of a large house. Tang went to the door and rang the bell. The door opened and Tang disappeared inside, reappearing a moment later and nodding to Susie. "OK, boys, I have two very high class ladies for you – very nice, no need to pay, I take care of business, you enjoy." The boys left the car expressing their thanks to Susie and vanished into the house.

We drove off and Susie put her hand in mine. "We alone again, Jake, and your friends will be happy tonight."

We arrived at the house. There were four minders around the front doorway, watching as people entered. Cars were dropping people off, one after the other. We entered a very crowded hallway – people in every corner, dressed to the nines, drinking champagne and enjoying themselves. I was feeling underdressed for this occasion, having no tie and jacket on.

Susie grabbed my hand shouting "Party time!" in my ear.

"Let's get upstairs, Susie. I've just spotted one of our officers – a Major – over there."

"Did he see you?"

"No, he wouldn't recognise me, but better not to chance it."

"Maybe you see him on TV later," she said with a smile. "Maybe into boys, yes?"

"Oh my God, what next?" I was glad to be in private with Susie, and we were soon relaxing in a hot oiled bath, getting the dirt and smell of the streets off our bodies. There was I, never thought the streets smelt before, couldn't say I'd noticed before – maybe I just smelt that way – anyway I wasn't complaining, and I was enjoying myself. We dried ourselves and I poured drinks and walked over to Susie, who was in the TV cupboard twiddling knobs and flicking from channel to channel.

"Anything good on?" I asked, as I handed her the glass.

"Not yet Jake." She was scanning outside the building. You could see for a good distance in both directions down the street. Cars were coming and going non-stop.

"Ever get raided by the police?"

"Never, too much high people here – including Chief of Police."

"Bloody outrageous the nerve of these people! Here they are, shagging each other and getting pissed out of their brains, and the poor rankers downtown getting the shit kicked out of them by the MPs for doing the same. There's no justice!"

"You're learning Jake, you smart cookie. Come, we make love."

She was just about to turn off the TV when I stopped her. In the room we were looking into there was a man dressed in a Sam Browne belt with his swagger stick in his hand, standing next to a bed with two boys tied across it. He was beating both of them with the stick. I looked at Susie – and she wasn't at all shocked.

"It's OK. He won't do them any damage. They like it: get paid plenty." The man turned in the direction of the camera. I was stuck for words – I looked and looked. "What's up, Jake?"

"I know this man. He's our padre – a minister of the church, an army Chaplin."

"So? He will be busy at confession!" said Susie, laughing.

"Well, church parade will never be the same again when the lads hear of this. Is anyone else watching this, Susie?"

"Yes, the control room downstairs, they see everything – even my room." I shot her a glance. "It's OK. I can switch it off when I'm in, but we need it for security when I'm in alone." We went back to the bedroom and got into bed. She turned to me and looked right into my eyes. "Jake, you ever kill anyone?"

"What kind of question is that? No I have not."

"Just a thought. You good shot."

"Yes, I'm a marksman, that's what I do best."

"You teach me, I can use handgun. You teach me how to use machine gun like I see in movies."

"I teach you sometime."

"You teach me tomorrow, Jake."

"I don't have a machine gun, and I'm not stealing one!"

"No need, Jake, I got."

"What are you talking about?"

"I got, OK. Tomorrow we go shooting, but now we make love." Before I could reply she stuck her tongue down my throat. That was the end of any more conversation.

Next morning we had breakfast on the balcony, then went downstairs, passing cleaners under the supervision of minders. Susie opened the door to the room that was used for the money counting, and headed for the far side – the wall was all panels. She lifted a small Buddha and pressed a button hidden under it, and a panel opened.

It was the door the two money men had entered by the last time I was in this room. So this was the control room, with two more TVs and an army radio like the one upstairs. The two money men stood up as we entered. "Good morning, Susie. Good morning, Jake." There was some Chinese chit-chat then one of them opened a door to a long corridor. There was a tall wine rack at the far end; one of the money men pulled on one side and it swung inward to reveal a flight of stairs going down to a cellar, with just one light-bulb hanging on a wire at the bottom. I followed Susie down the stairs. It was cold, just bare stone walls but no damp, piles of old wicker boxes and a well-stocked wine rack. I was expecting her to open a box and pull out a rusting sub-machine gun. As we stood in the middle of the cellar, I put my arms around her waist.

"Not now, Jake. Business first." There was a noise of electric motors then the far wall began to move to the right.

"What is it, Susie?" The noise stopped, then bright, flickering strip lights came on and my chin dropped in amazement.

"Bloody hell! I walked into a large room, must have been the whole basement of the house. Rack upon rack of guns, all spotless – mostly British. Lee Enfields, Sten and Owen guns, good old Thompsons, Lanchesters, Brens, mortars, grenades, Mills 36 – a whole barrelful, some Jap handguns and stick grenades, even a flamethrower of US origin.

"See? I tell you I have gun."

"Have gun? Looks like Ali Baba's cave for the forty thieves! You have enough for an army."

"We have much more in other places."

"How did you get it?"

"My father was very enterprising when the British ran away from the Japanese and left us alone. He did deal with British army and hid weapons before the surrender. Then when the wind came from the west again, we steal Jap weapons." She picked up a Sten. It was in mint condition. I checked it – the barrel was spotless. "We have them cleaned and oiled every month. We take this one, and a rifle, and a few grenades. OK, Jake?"

"OK, boss!" She turned and grinned.

"*Christ, I should report this,*" I was thinking. "*I can't. I'm in too deep; they have too much on me. The army would jail me and throw away the key. If I had reported it earlier I wouldn't be seeing this now. Shit!*"

My head was spinning – "Keep your mouth shut," I kept telling myself. "*These people wouldn't hesitate to have me killed if they thought I was a threat.*"

We picked up the weapons and ammo and headed back the way

we came. Back in the control room the two minders took the weapons and we went back upstairs to the bedroom. "Susie, do you have any more surprises for me? Why didn't you tell me before what you're mixed up in? I find out one piece at a time."

"Better that way, Jake, we can trust you better. If you went to the police or any authority we would know, and father would have you killed. We know you have not, and that is why I show you this today." She was out of her clothes and changing into a sand coloured bush shirt, trousers and canvas boots. I changed into clean olive greens, T-shirt, bush hat and shades.

"Don't think too much, Jake. You see last night how your masters treat your friends; they think we are all peasants. You smart, Jake Two Knife. We are going to an island off Singapore, not far, and then you can show me how good you are and teach me to use machine gun."

"I hope there is no intention to use these weapons against British Forces, Susie?"

"If there was I would not have let you see so much. The British will leave in due course, you will see. No need to fight – just some riots and demonstrations, very soon, but no big trouble."

A car was waiting outside for us with a driver and one of the minders. It was Tang. "Good day, Mr Jake."

"Very nice day," I replied, and got in. We headed for Changi creek, boarded a waiting sampan, and made ourselves comfortable in the bow.

The sampan headed out to sea, and I put my arm around Susie and pulled her in to me, her hair blowing in the wind. I noticed her perfume was stronger than the smell of the salt air. Then I suddenly remembered the weapons. I was about to speak, but she knew what I was going to say and pointed to another sampan.

"Guns are over there."

"Oh, boy, you think of everything."

"Many police patrol boats around. We take no risk. We transfer guns in one hour when we reach the island."

"What if the police intercept them?"

"No problem, we have more guns."

"But what about the boat people?"

"They get paid, dare not tell. They are expendable – we are all expendable."

"Bloody hell, Susie – these are just poor fishermen!"

"That's how it is here, Jake. Get used to it."

Well, that was me put in my place, so I sat thinking this over and said nothing. We arrived at the island and Tang unloaded the weapons from the other sampan. The three of us watched as the two sampans departed in different directions around the island, to check that all was clear. I set up some coconuts on a log as targets, and checked out an old pillbox, a remnant of WW2, by which time the first sampan had returned. All was clear, the other sampan would continue patrolling till we finished. I took the Sten gun and some fishing cord, and did a lashing around the barrel just forward of the extractor. I explained to Susie and Tang that many men had lost fingers with this weapon, because their hands would slip with the sweat and vibration, and their fingers would be fed into the breech. The binding would stop that happening. I loaded three magazines of 9 mm.

"This is a close-range weapon and is used in short bursts. The targets are only twenty-five yards away – beyond seventy yards don't bother. You first Susie. Now, hold it like this in the shoulder, lean forward and pull the butt in, look through the sight at the target and squeeze the trigger." The first burst hit the coconut. "Now the next one. Very good. I think you've done this before."

"No never!"

"OK, let's go in closer and fire from the hip. This takes a lot of practice. Let me show you." I took the gun, changed the magazine and fired a burst of fifteen rounds. "Now you can see the effect at closer range, a longer burst, just like you were using a hosepipe in the garden".

She practised until she was satisfied, and then we turned our attention to the old pillbox. "I'm going to show you how to throw a grenade. First along the straight. Let's use them with the pins in." Soon they were flying in all directions, landing in the sand. "Straight arm and throw over that log. You got it do it again. OK, Tang, collect them up. Susie, I'm going to prime now."

"Oh! to make bang?"

"Yes, watch me as I do this – very dangerous – this is a four second detonator: use only forefinger and thumb as the heat of the hand could set it off. Right, let's go to the pillbox and have a look inside." It was empty. "Susie, stand on the right of the door with your back to the wall and don't move." I was on the other side of the doorway, as I was left handed, and pulled the pin out with my right hand. I threw the grenade round the corner into the pillbox. One, two, three, bang – and a shower of grit and dust burst out of the doorway. Susie was giggling, "My turn now." I passed her a grenade. She pulled the pin and sent it through the doorway: one, two, three, bang!

"Have another go, Susie." I handed her another grenade. One, two, three, bang. "Well done. Now if that grenade didn't go off you should never go and try and find out why – stay well clear."

"I understand," she replied with a giggle.

We took the rest of the grenades down to the water's edge, pulling the pins and throwing them out to sea as far as we could. The explosions caused white foaming waterspouts and killed enough fish to delight the fishermen.

"Jake, I want to see you use this." She lifted the Lee Enfield sniper rifle, already fitted with the sniper scope and passed it to me. Some of the coconuts were still on the log two hundred yards away, but I saw an old fishing box with lettering on it – this would do for me to zero in the rifle. I lay down in the sand and making myself comfortable took aim at the letter 'Y' on the box. My first round landed ten inches to the left of the 'Y'. I adjusted the scope, fired again, and my shot landed two inches to the left. I adjusted again and the next shot was on the 'Y'. Two more shots also hit the 'Y'. Now I reloaded and turned my attention to the coconuts – five shots rang out and five coconuts flew into the air!

"I'm impressed, Jake."

"Let's try a little further, say four hundred yards."

"You're kidding me, Jake!"

"No, I can do this – this rifle is good for seven hundred yards in the right hands."

Tang was setting up the targets while we walked along the beach counting the yards, then we sat down and waited for Tang to join us. I got downloaded and fired ten rounds scoring ten out of ten. I stood up and Susie threw her arms around my neck. "You make me very happy, that was very good, Jake. We must go now as it is getting late."

We boarded the sampan, to the smell of fish cooking and, once under way, we sat down to a meal of rice and fresh fish prepared by the crew – it was excellent.

It was growing dark by the time we got to Changi creek. Tang drove us to Selarang Barracks, stopping short of the gate. "Jake, I will see you tomorrow at the bar in Changi at two o'clock, OK?"

"That's fine with me, I enjoyed today very much." I watched as the car disappeared in the direction of the city.

I walked back into camp, bypassing the guardroom on a well-worn track. The camp was in turmoil: trucks backed-up to stores, ammo boxes being loaded, people running about shouting orders – not like a weekend. I entered my barrack block, climbed the stairs and came face to face with my platoon Sergeant.

"Where the hell have you been?"

"Downtown, I don't have to be back till first parade tomorrow."

"Well get your gear together, soldier, because we are off to war. Now move your arse!"

I looked at the rest of the lads fitting their kit and started getting mine together. "Bring me up to date Raggie, I seem to have missed something."

"All I know is we're going to RAF Changi for 1930 hours tonight. I don't know the destination, but the lads think it's Vietnam, as that is what we have been training for."

"Shit! I should have stayed out till the morning!"

"Plenty of the lads are still downtown – the MPs are rounding them up and getting them back to camp as we speak." I got my gear together then went off to find Sunshine and Chalky.

I found Sunshine sitting on his bed cleaning his rifle; Chalky was there all packed ready to go.

"I must get a message to Susie."

"You haven't got time, Jake."

"I'm off down Changi."

"I'm coming with you, Jake, just to make certain you come back."

We took off down the back track, got a taxi into Changi and went to the bar. I wrote a note and handed it to the bar boy and asked him to get it to Susie fast. We took another taxi to bring us back to camp.

"Are you at the airport same as us, Sunshine?"

"No, we're going by sea with the navy."

"What's going on? Looks like Alpha Company is the cutting edge, Sunshine. Hope to see you there, wherever it is! By the way, how did you make out the other night with those women Susie fixed you up with?"

"Tell you later, Jake, time to go." We paid the taxi driver and made our way back to our platoon areas.

Chapter 5

Brunei

Hostage Situation – December 1962

We arrived at RAF Changi at 1930 hours – it was December 8th, 1962. Everything was in chaos: RAF officers and NCOs running about flapping, taking families off a flight that was bound for the UK – wives and kids, who had less idea of what was going on than we had!

We boarded the Britannia aircraft, ammo boxes stacked in the aisle; every seat and box had a Jock sitting on it. We taxied out and took off, the intercom clicked on.

"This is the Captain speaking. I would like to welcome you aboard this flight to 'you-know-where'. Flight time is approximately three hours, haversack rations will be issued shortly. Sit back and enjoy the flight." We were still none the wiser about our final destination.

I checked my rifle for the tenth time that night then sharpened my two knives, bayonet and machete. The haversack rations arrived and, as these had been packed by the RAF, we thought there might be a treat – bread and spam, one hard-boiled egg, one packet of Smith's crisps and a Mars bar.

"Well, we just can't escape the same old rations we've had since we joined up. Bloody marvellous, next stop, Glasgow!" said some comedian.

About two hours later and just as everyone had dropped off to sleep: 'Click' – "This is your Captain, we are now near to our destination. Time check – '5, 4, 3, 2, 1' – time now 2312 hours. When I land I will taxi close to the terminal building. The emergency escape system nearest will be opened, all personnel will deplane and run towards the light in the doorway of the building. Take all your equipment with you as I will be leaving immediately. Thank you, good luck, God be with you all." '*Click*'.

We started to bank. I heard the landing-gear lock into place. NCOs passed instructions to their sections. "Webbing and steel helmets on, full magazines on rifles."

Lights dimmed. '*Click*'. "Brace, brace, brace!" came the order. We hit hard, and quickly taxied to the terminal building. Emergency doors opened. "Go, go, go!" We made our way to the exits and jumped, sliding down the emergency chutes. My feet hit the ground and I started to run for the light in the doorway I tripped over something and got back on my feet to shouts of, "Get down!" as I entered the building.

I threw myself to the floor and slid to a halt against a booking counter. Other bodies were doing the same. There was an oil lamp burning, and torch lights. "Where are we?" I shouted.

"Brunei," shouted an RAF man.

"Where the hell is Brunei, never heard of it!" someone said.

"What's happening?" I asked. "What did I fall over out there?"

The RAF chap said, "Dead Gurkha soldiers, snipers out there!"

I heard the thunder of engines as our aircraft departed. We got organised and made a move, under cover of darkness and some smoke. We reached a large shed close to the edge of the runway. More troops started to arrive, and soon were dispersed around the airfield. The company commander called a briefing and told us the news. "The Sultanate of Brunei has been attacked by rebels under the command of Azahari, a local troublemaker. Government establishments, including those operated by other European nations, have been attacked. The rebels have taken many hostages and seized the Shell oilfield here at a place called Seria. We have been tasked to deal with the problem. Gurkha troops were ordered in to stop the rioting and have been ambushed with loss of life. British oil workers have been taken hostage in Seria and held in the local Panaga Police Station. Their families are in danger of being killed by the rebels; we are going to get them out. Seventy-five men of Alpha Company will fly into Seria in a Beverly transport plane. The runway is grass. I have been informed that there could be up to three hundred enemy troops supported by rebels."

"The other half of Alpha Company will be going into the football field on the other side of the town in twelve twin Pioneer aircraft. Objective – to rescue some forty-six European hostages being held at the Panaga Police Station. The rebels will be between us – with the sea over here, and the swamps behind the town here. You have thirty minutes to eat and get ready. All NCOs report to me now. Carry on."

I got my mess kit out and made a hot meal, and I checked my rifle. Everyone was doing the same. The NCOs returned to their sections. "We are going in musketry order: belt kit only, ammo and water bottles, first aid dressings – no packs, no food, they will join us later. One hundred and sixty rounds each rifleman – that is all."

I managed to stuff my camera into a belt pouch along with hard tack, biscuits and boiled sweets, and then I watched the lads. Everyone was quiet now, with their own thoughts. I thought, "If this is it, I'm going to take as many as I can with me. Seventy-five of us against some three hundred, with only one hundred and sixty rounds each, and not a single grenade!"

A Beverly transport plane arrived and taxied up to the shed. We climbed into the cargo hold and were told to hold onto the wall bars. All grabbed hold as we started to taxi: there were no doors and no seats. We took off and travelled the sixty miles along the coastline, then we had to wait for the Twin Pins to reach their area on the other side of the town. I looked at the Sergeant Major, whose handlebar moustache was drooping, and sweat was dripping off the end. He caught my eye and I burst out laughing. I could read his lips but not hear his voice over the din of the engines – "You bastard!" he mouthed, I think he must have remembered the night I cut of half his moustache while he slept, I must've been the only one who did laugh on that flight – I couldn't resist it.

"Here we go." We came in low over the tree line and dropped down onto the grass runway; the brakes came on and the props went into reverse. "Go!" We were still moving. I jumped and rolled twice, with my rifle trucked across my middle. I was third man out. In front of me I saw the earth jump into the air as incoming rounds patterned the area. The fire was coming from the edge of the airfield. The Beverly was already taking off in the same run, having unloaded all troops and equipment. Fighter jets from HMS *Hermes* came out of nowhere and raked both sides of the field, driving back the snipers. We formed an extended line five yards apart and advanced down the grass runway, with our piper playing *Highland Laddie*. This was unbelievable!

I could see the enemy six hundred yards ahead jumping up and down like monkeys. Rounds were cracking past me, some throwing earth high in the air. I looked along the line to the right – no one had yet been hit – and we kept going. We were now at four hundred yards, and just past the control tower. I looked to my left, down a track past the Bren group. "Enemy left!"

We swung round as fire section and laid down fire. I heard the platoon Sergeant shouting, "Right flanking!" Rounds hit the ground around me as I moved to follow the Bren group at the double, down the track beside the control tower. We reached the main road and the Bren group jumped into the ditch. I was just about to follow when a rebel in olive green, wearing a helmet of American issue, popped up from the ditch opposite and opened up in my direction. I felt the hot blast go to the right of my head. He turned to run. I fired three rounds, all hitting him. I went down into the ditch, rounds hammering the ground above my head – someone had me in their sights. I crawled to my right, towards the Bren group, who were returning fire. The right flanking attack had taken the enemy by surprise and we were taking prisoners. Fire was still coming from ahead of us. We attacked head on with the bayonet, and resistance stopped. I spotted trail marks through the waist-high grass; then it split into four. We had no grenades so three of us proceeded down the trail, weapons at the ready, then all hell broke loose as we spotted four of the enemy – gunfire in both directions. We killed all four – how we never got hit I don't know!

Back on the road again, the prisoners were sitting along the verge with their hands on their heads. We quickly formed up to advance on a Bailey bridge leading to Seria town. We were point section, the cutting edge, and I was on the right-hand side of the road. A mix of vehicles came in our direction, flying Kalamantan flags. The first truck was shot off the road; the second was a Land-Rover pick-up truck with a Bren gun mounted over the cab – the gunner was shot dead. Our platoon Sergeant Jake Lewis ran up to the driver's side of the vehicle and shot the driver between the eyes with his Sterling sub-machine gun, sending a spray of blood and bone all over the cab. Raggie opened the other door and told the occupant to get out. The man didn't move – he was terrified and couldn't understand. The order was repeated. "Get out, you black git!" The man was dragged out, and two inches of bayonet was stuck through his shoulder as he went for a knife in his belt.

The Company had a good body count for the first day: over forty enemies killed for three walking wounded. We were extremely lucky. We found only armed rebels and not the expected Indonesian troops we'd been led to believe were there. It's a strange thing, but when the wounded enemy were being brought through our lines, there were Jocks handing out sweeties, feeling sorry for the guys they'd been shooting at twenty minutes before – sort of 'cut them up with a machine gun then offer a Band Aid'. Unknown to us people were being killed just a few miles ahead of us: locals who refused to join the rebellion, people running in fear, mothers and children locking their doors and hiding. Trigger-happy bands of young men brought a cloak of terror over the population going from house to house demanding firearms and food. Most European males were held in the Panaga Prison but their wives and children were in their homes hiding and praying.

We made it to the Anduki river bridge on the afternoon of Saturday 9th December and dug in – down one foot, and we hit water. The rain started, and we were waist-deep in water in no time. It was now dark, but ahead of us we could see the flare stacks of the oilfields. The rain stopped, and mosquitoes and sand flies came out to eat us. No rations, only hard army biscuits – one packet each and the water we carried. The river behind us was oil-contaminated.

The second day Sunday 10th December dawned, and already we were puffed up like Michelin men; dirty mud-ingrained, hungry and very tired. By midday hot food arrived in hay boxes – burnt Irish stew! We had no mess tins, knife, fork or spoon – our kit was still sixty miles behind us. We ripped the liners out of our steel helmets and used them to hold stew, and used our dirty hands to scoop up the slop. I suddenly realised we were all stinking like a monsoon ditch in a heatwave.

Alpha Company fought its way into the town with little air cover from the RAF. We had to clear the town, house by house, shop by shop. We helped ourselves to canned food, mostly Chinese. I needed film for my camera and I soon found a Kodak shop – already looted.

We got to the car showrooms, broke in, and drove new Land-Rovers and any suitable vehicle straight through the plate glass windows.

After a long battle with elements of Alpha Company under the command of Maj. I.D. Cameron the Panaga Prison was stormed, earning him a Military Cross. The hostages were freed. One of the hostages had been killed on the December 8th at the hands of the rebels; the rest of the male hostages went to rejoin their families. On December 11th, 1962 we evacuated some families by chopper. I carried a small girl (then aged three) kicking and screaming to a helicopter; little did I know that her father's body lay just ten feet away as I handed her over to the aircrew of that helicopter. She was joined by her mother, her two brothers and baby sister, and taken away from the terror that was Seria.

Now that Seria was secure, we moved on to the next town of Kuala Balait, and a much smaller amount of gunfire was exchanged. We fought our way to the Police Station, a large wooden building – or what was left of it – with more bullet-holes than timber. Starting to cross the road, at the double, we came under fire. The double turned into a sprint as bullets ripped up tarmac around our feet – funny how fast you can run when in danger! We made it to the cover of some shops, dived inside and lay on the floor, trying to get our breath in the hot, dusty air.

More fire – not at us this time. Another section was on the receiving end, but we had spotted the fire coming from the Mosque; high up on a tower a lone rebel armed with a machine gun was firing at anything that moved. We opened fire with everything we had and the other sections joined in too. The enemy gun fell silent but there was the odd shot still coming from the Mosque from a few diehard rebels. The order came to fix bayonets and advance. As soon as the opposition saw what was coming, and heard the sound of our lone piper, they came out with hands held high. "What a load of fairies – spoilt our fun!" I heard someone say. However, we had come to the end of another day without casualties and the rebellion came to an end, as they all do.

There was still the threat of invasion from Indonesia. We were split up into patrols of six men to guard telecom, police station, powerhouse and any landing areas. The Platoon Commander took six of us out to a grass landing strip one afternoon, near a place called Miri. "I want you to dig in three slit trenches – one down there at the seaward end of the runway, one halfway along this side, and the third at the other end. One Bren gun at each end and two riflemen in centre trench. If there's an airborne invasion from Indonesia it will be of Brigade strength, about ten to twelve thousand men. I want you to hold here until relieved. Radio checks every two hours from Company HQ – listen out on radio, any questions?"

"Sir, we've only one hundred and sixty rounds per man and no grenades".

"That's why you have a bayonet, soldier, and chances are nothing is going to happen." He jumped into his vehicle and took off in a cloud of dust.

"Any good news, boys?" said Raggie.

"Hold till relieved."

"Saw that in a movie once: something about Korea, there were no survivors."

"That's fine, why us?"

"Because we are here, no one else."

"Listen," I said, "if we want to get out of this without getting our heads blown off, we just do what we've been told. But, if that first aircraft arrives, and, God, I hope for our sakes it doesn't, we fire everything into it then run like hell into that jungle over there. Let's get dug in, then we'll make an RV in the jungle on the other side of the strip, so we can link up if the shit hits the fan. We look out for us, nobody else is going to."

We spent five days and nights there on cold rations. The only check was by radio, to say we were still in place and all was quiet. The following week our Platoon was on coastal watch, high up on a jungle-covered cliff top. We were looking for a submarine that had been seen by some locals, supposedly landing stores a few days before. We watched for a week – not a sign of any vessels. All we got was very wet every night and covered in leeches, spending the daytime burning the things off. We returned to Miri to rejoin the Company and reorganise ourselves with new jungle greens and all the other equipment that needed replacing.

The threat was over for the time being. Now it was time to collect weapons from local people and destroy them before they fell into the wrong hands. Notices were displayed with reward money for any weapons; five hundred dollars for a rifle, two hundred for a hand gun, fifty for grenades. By this time I'd linked up with Sunshine and Chalky. As soon as we saw how much was going to be paid, we wanted our share. The three of us got friendly with a couple of locals, who would hand in items we gave them, get the cash, and we would split it up between us.

We got to know the locals, and in particular the girls and it wasn't long before they were entertaining the troops, earning a fortune.

One morning a female, accompanied by a police officer, came to complain that the Jocks had robbed her. The Company Commander saw her off with, "Well, if she associated with the Jocks, she can't expect anything else." What had happened was that the woman had done the rounds of the Company, and the last two Jocks – Glasgow lads, no less – had relieved her of her hard-earned dollars and kicked her out. God knows how many she infected, but the sick parade was getting bigger every day.

Now another infection was starting to bother us – the confrontation with President Sukarno of Indonesia; now the new Federation of Malaysia had begun in earnest.

Intelligence reports received indicated that communist cells were operating in our area, recruiting fighters for the Indonesian army. Their location was on an island, surrounded by mangrove swamp, about six hours along the coast by sea from our position. A plan was hatched at short notice to attack the island with the whole of 'A' Company.

We boarded an old cement barge after dark one evening, and set sail for the island. It was not long before every man in the flat-bottomed barge was sea sick from the pounding we got from the weather. We arrived in the area of the island well before first light, and boarded out inflatable boats for the short sea crossing into the mangrove swamps. We paddled all the way, in order not to attract attention. We landed up to our knees in thick mud but soon got onto firm ground with the help of our local trackers. Once near the village, we waited for the first sign of daylight then moved in. The enemy was taken by surprise, and not a shot fired. We returned to our base with our prisoners and handed them over to the police.

Now it was time for us to return to Singapore for a well earned rest!

* * *

The order had gone out if the British attacked: all hostages were to be killed including their families on December 12th.

It was all over on the December 11th.

Names of the Hostages

Clifford A.M. Joseph (Killed evening of December 8th, 1962

V. Abraham	T. Lingman	H.F Eighme
A. Allan	L. MacKechnie	H.F. McDonald
A.E.O. Bennett	A.L.E. Meacher	Capt. R.K. Brown
B.J. Blanche	R.C. Morgan	Capt. A. Oprel
G. Bomhof	A. Rawson	Capt. P. Sipek
J.W. Bloemendal	T.G. Rea	A.J. Ker-Lindsay

R.S.P. Clark

P.W. de Waard

C.M.W. Fern

C.W. Hall

O.M. Hampton

P.M. Hillier

D.R. Humphrey

T.J. Joseph

G.L. Kirby

A.F. Knights

Leong Yat Chor

D.M. Sargeant

M.C.C. Rodenburge

H.F. Williamson

Dr J.F. Brondijk

Capt. W.J. Davise

Dr A.C. MacLean

H. Firman

H. McAnulty

J. Oliver

R. Brunet de Roche Brene

R. Cortenbach

R.F.W. Fisher

A.E. Gaughan

A.Coy. boarding Twin Pins at Brunei for assault on Seria
December 1962

Beverly aircraft ready for attack on Anduki
December 1962

This time it's for real

The sports field at Seria and a very muddy landing for the Twin Pins

*Raggie and Jake crawl out of a muddy trench at the Anduki bridge
December 10th 1962*

No 1 Platoon A. Coy enter swamps behind Seria

A bulldozer used by rebels to gain entry to
police station at Kuala Balait

A Highlander stands guard as local police
come out after the fight is over

Fire fight at Tutong
December 1962

Patrol around Seria
December 1962

Returning to HMS Albion *after Brunei Rebellion*

We depart from Brunei and board HMS Albion
for our return to Singapore

Chapter 6

War in the Manor

I t was only on our return to Singapore that we realised how much weight we'd lost and how pale we looked. It was noticeable that the infighting between the older Camerons and Seaforths had stopped, and there was a new air about the regiment. Everyone had a story to tell, and there would be much drinking and banter until our next mission.

It was a chance for Chalky, Sunshine and me to get together for a good chat – we had not seen much of each other in the last few months. It wasn't long before women came into the conversation. "You never told me how you two got on with the girls Susie fixed you up with."

"Well, Jake," said Sunshine, "it was a good night. They were high-class hookers, and their husbands were away at sea."

"They were very good, Jake," said Chalky, "but we thought you were going to fix us up, permanent like."

"I will ask Susie when I see her. I don't think she'll forget."

I sent a message to the bar in Changi to inform Susie I was back, and would be at our meeting place on Saturday night. I arrived early, and saw Tang standing there. "Hi, Jake, how are you?"

"OK, Tang."

"Susie come soon, we wait."

Susie appeared out of the Orchard Hotel, all smiles. She was looking as good as ever, dressed in a black silk trouser suit, pearl earrings and choker, and very inviting red lips. "Hi, Susie, how are you?"

"I am very well, Jake, but I miss you bad. We go home, yes?"

"OK, let's go!" We jumped into the car and Tang drove off. "How's business been?"

Susie looked at me. "There's been some trouble on the collection of the rounds. One of our men was stabbed and another had his arm broken. My father ordered Tang and some of our friends to take care of things."

"Was it a brothel or a gambling joint?" I asked.

"It was a gambling joint. Now it's closed – we fire-bombed it."

"Was anyone killed, or is that stupid question?"

"Oh yes, I think about fifteen. Is that right, Tang?"

"Yes, that's right. I know, I read newspaper!"

"Well, nothing changes with you, Susie!"

She laughed and squeezed my hand. "My father is at home just now. You can meet him tomorrow." We had a very relaxing bath and then dressed and went downstairs for an evening meal – I was even starting to smell a like human again.

When we entered the dining room, Mai Ling was sitting at a table – she got up to greet us. "So nice to see you, Jake. You are well?"

"Yes, I'm very well, and pleased to be here. You are as beautiful as ever Mai Ling," I replied, and took my seat. The staff laid a meal fit for a king.

The girls wanted to know all about my adventures and the talk went on till late. The house was strangely quiet for a Saturday night. "Why so quiet tonight, girls?"

"The business I told you about earlier. My father says we must be careful until things quieten down. Susie told me about your friends and that they want girlfriends."

"Yes, Mai Ling, that's right."

"I would like to meet them. Can we arrange something?"

"I would think they'd be delighted."

We retired, slept well, woke early and had breakfast on the balcony as the sun was coming up like a ball of fire.

It was mid-morning when we went downstairs and into a room I had not seen before. It was wood-panelled like the others, with a strong smell of leather and tobacco. The furniture was bright red leather, and the tables and sideboard were black hardwood with gold dragon designs. As I looked around the room, a high-backed chair swivelled round. I was taken aback as the man in the chair stood up. He was all of six foot and well built, with a soft round face and a pencil-line moustache.

Susie said, "Good morning, father, are you well? This is Jake, I told you about him."

"Ah, yes, Jake. It is a pleasure to meet you. I have heard much from Susie." His English was perfect. There was no expression on his face; his eyes were almost European, but black and piercing. I took his hand, which was limp and cold as I gave him a firm handshake.

"I'm pleased to meet you at last," I lied. I knew I was treading on dangerous ground.

"Please sit awhile. I am very much away on business, but I hear how helpful you have been and I like to show my appreciation. I have arranged for you and Susie to stay at the best hotel in Penang for a week as soon as you can organise some leave – how about the end of this month?"

"Sounds good to me, sir."

"Susie tells me there is business to be had in Borneo?"

"Sorry, sir, but you have lost me?"

"Girls for the soldiers," he said.

"Ah, I understand now."

"You can tell me the best places and how many troops in each area. I am convinced we can make a profit. Give all the information to Susie. I am leaving for Saigon this afternoon. There are some GIs with plenty of dollars to spend," he said, smiling. "I hope to see you again soon." He turned his chair away and we backed out of the door. He certainly was not concerned that I was sleeping with his daughter.

We left for town with Tang. Susie wanted to do some shopping in Orchard Road. When we arrived it was pouring – the monsoon season had started. Tang drove up on the pavement so we were under cover and Susie wouldn't get wet. We went inside into a fashion house, where she ordered this and that then it was make-up. I was glad I wasn't paying!

"Let's go to the teahouse, Jake, and you can give me all the details father was asking for. By the way, I deposited the other half of your money into your account while you were away." I thanked her. "Now I want to get you some new clothes before we go to Penang."

"Nothing too fancy," I said, "or questions will be asked."

"You can keep them at my place, OK?" We went into a shop for men, the sort of place I would never dream of going into. An evening suit was fitted, shirts, ties, trousers, beachwear, shoes, sandals and a real pair of shades.

"Susie! There are no holes in the pockets for my knives!" She just burst out laughing.

We returned to the house, spent the afternoon lazing about, and then went down for the evening meal. Mai Ling was sitting at the table, and started a conversation as soon as we sat down. "Jake, can you bring your two friends downtown next weekend?"

"I'll see. I'm certain we can fix it."

"Good, we can meet at the Cellar Bar, Collier Quay. Tell your friends not to wear army uniforms." This was a strange turn of events. I had not yet seen Mai Ling in the company of a man, but the lads would be delighted.

As soon as I got back to camp I found Sunshine and Chalky scooping it up in the NAAFI. I joined them, and waited to see if they would ask about the girls. The chat went on about everything, but just before closing time I said, "By the way, it's on for next weekend."

The two of them looked at me. Chalky said, "What the hell are you talking about?"

"I've fixed the girls for next weekend."

Their faces were a picture. "Jake, you bugger! You waited all night to tell us that?"

"Friday night we go down to the Brit Club – no uniforms, 1930 hours. We'll go to meet the girls at the Cellar Bar then we'll be going on to Raffles."

"We can't go in there! It'll cost a fortune!"

"Who said you had to pay? Just be cool and pretend it's the norm. The girls will take care of everything."

"Officers and their wives go in there," said Sunshine, a look of concern on his face.

"They're not any better than you, are they? I've seen things you wouldn't believe."

"Come on, tell us, Jake!" So I told them about the chaplain and the two boys, and the surveillance cameras. "You kinky bugger!" said Chalky.

"Have you heard about this Profumo scandal, and Christine and Mandy sleeping with everybody in the government?" said Sunshine.

"Kinky tarts! They'd do good business here!"

"The government wants to know if the morale in the forces has been affected," said Chalky.

"Yes! It's gone up!"

"What a load of wankers, as if the Jocks care!"

Friday came, and we descended on the Brit Club, looking clean and smart. We had an hour to kill so we got the pints in. "Better not get pissed," I said. "The girls won't be amused if you can't get it up." At 1930 hours we got a taxi to the Cellar Bar, and waited and waited.

"They aren't coming," said Sunshine. "Let's go back to the club and get pissed." Just at that moment the yellow car pulled up.

"It's them," I told the lads, and their attitude changed immediately to proper gentlemen as they helped the girls out. Mai Ling was there with a girl called Ruby – she was a stunner too. Chalky put his arm around her and she smiled. Sunshine was a bit slow, but Mai Ling soon sorted that. Susie was already hanging on my arm. All three were dressed in full-length Chinese dresses and well made up – must have been in the paint shop all afternoon! We had a drink in the Cellar Bar then Mai Ling said, "We go to Raffles now."

We trooped out, got into Tang's car, and headed for Raffles. As we approached the front door of Raffles, there was a giant of an Indian doorman on duty. He opened the door without a word. We entered, and Susie headed in the direction of reception. We all followed. She was speaking to the receptionist in Chinese and obtained a key. In the lounge bar, the Singapore slings were ordered and we settled in like gentlemen. There was plenty of chat, then Mai Ling said, "Let's go," so we trooped upstairs and found the room. It was very luxurious, with two bedrooms – both with king size beds; the lounge was large, with a table and leather chairs; a pull down bed in one wall; and three bottles of champagne, on ice, and a full drinks cabinet. We got well drunk – including the girls.

Ruby turned the lights down low. It wasn't long before they started to strip to the sound of rock music. The frolicking started, and ended in a real gang bang. I woke up at some stage of the night, Susie curled up on my right and Mai Ling on my left – all three of us naked, but now I couldn't tell one from the other! Then, in the gloom, I saw Sunshine pissing into a large potted plant.

"Where's Chalky?" I asked.

"In the bathroom, with a woman!" I looked at the other bed. Ruby was sound asleep.

"What woman?" I asked.

"Some woman knocked on the door. Chalky opened it and a woman fell in, totally pissed, looking for her husband. Some officer's wife I think. She was all over Chalky, so Chalky screwed her and then she started to vomit. Chalky showed her into the bathroom."

I got up and put my trousers on. As I got to the bathroom door, it opened. "Give me a hand, Jake. Have a look in the corridor – see if it's clear." She was dressed in a slinky gold cocktail dress, must have got lost. She would have been about twenty-five and a good looking lady. We quickly placed her in one of the large armchairs in the corridor and went back into our room. "Hope I don't meet her at breakfast," said Chalky.

"Don't worry, we'll have breakfast in the room." I crawled in between the two girls – still didn't know who was who – and went to sleep. When I woke, Susie was sitting up in bed next to me.

"Good morning, Jake."

"Good morning, Susie. Is Mai Ling still asleep?"

"Yes Jake, why?"

"Oh, nothing."

"I know what you are thinking, Jake. Is this really me?" I laughed, and got into the shower with Susie – at least I think it was Susie!

When we returned to the room the others were up. What a mess! We scrambled around clearing the decks and phoned down for breakfast. By the time it arrived we looked respectable again. Mai Ling phoned down for Tang and we left an hour later. We went to Orchard Road, and Susie and I left the other four to make their own arrangements. We went round the shops, had coffee and Susie suggested we go back to her place.

Tang was waiting for us out front. He had bad news: one of the brothels had been burned down, and a bar had been bombed by a gang from the Jalan Basir area. Susie was furious.

"We will avenge this. We will burn them out. My father will have them all killed for this outrage."

"Susie, calm down and think this through," I said. "I know how you feel. Just slow down, let's get the rest of the story."

We went home with Tang chatting all the way, but I could understand only a little. There was a council of war waiting for us at the house: about fifteen men in the front reception area. Susie said, "Jake, take my key and go upstairs. I will see you later." This meeting was not for me – or she didn't want to be explaining our relationship. I filled the bath, climbed in, and just started thinking about what was going to happen next. Susie came in and began to strip to get in with me.

"That was quick, Susie."

"Yes, I told them to wait as my father will be here tomorrow. If we attack them they will know it is us, they would recognise our men. I wanted to get your thinking on this, Jake."

"This gang – you know who they are, what premises they have? All you need is people they would not expect or know."

She was quiet for a while, seeming to enjoy the bath then she smiled. "Jake! You could do it!"

"What?" I said.

"Yes. You and your friends would not be known to them. You could go in as customers. They always like servicemen – that's how they make their living after all. Let's think about it."

"I have, Susie. The lads won't do this."

"They would for five thousand dollars each."

"Holy shit!"

"You go ask them, Jake. Make a plan, and I will get it approved by father."

"I don't believe I'm doing this." I got dried, dressed and Tang took me back to camp.

It was only Sunday night, and no sign of the other two so I went to the NAAFI, bought a beer and sat with some of the other lads from my Platoon, catching up on the latest goings-on. Two hours later Chalky and Sunshine appeared, grinning from ear to ear.

"Best weekend ever!" said Chalky, as they got beers and sat down.

"Well, boys, I have a proposition for you. Let's move tables."

"What now, Jake?" I told them what had happened and what I'd been asked to do. I didn't mention money. "Bloody hell, Jake! We can't start a war!"

Then I said, "For five thousand dollars each?"

"Why not?" said Chalky, with a grin.

"I'm in," said Sunshine, "how shall we do it?"

"I was coming to that. I didn't tell you before, but below the house there are enough arms and explosives for an army, including mines and grenades." Just a look of surprise on the two faces opposite me.

"So that's why you didn't want to tell us. What else are you hiding?" said Sunshine.

"Nothing else, lads – promise. I want us to benefit from this with the minimal amount of risk. We don't have to be there, just make the bombs and have them delivered. First, we don't have to steal anything from the army – that's a plus. We take four five-gallon cooking oil drums – the type with the six-inch diameter screw lid on top. We get the explosive from old anti-tank mines and a grenade for a detonator, and wire a safety-pin up to the lid. When someone turns the lid anti-clockwise, it will withdraw the safety-pin, releasing the striker to ignite the fuse – you know the rest. Susie will get someone to deliver the bombs, and we just wait for the results."

We sat there grinning at each other, then Sunshine said something strange, "If get killed, I want to go home."

"If any of us get killed, they'll plant us here," said Chalky.

"All right then, something of us must go home. Let's promise each other that, even if it's just a gesture, even a handful of earth or something that belonged to us, whatever it is, we put it in the church at Fort George, Inverness." We looked at each other and then joined hands. "Let's drink to it – a long and happy life!"

On Sunday I contacted Susie and got the go-ahead. Susie would get Tang to take the materials to the island with the pillbox, and arrange transport for us next Saturday. I informed the lads and we went to Changi Quay. Tang was waiting for us, the sampans ready to sail: all the gear on one, us on the other. We boarded, and moved off without incident. The sea was a little choppy but we reached the island and were glad to get ashore. We followed Tang to the pillbox. We had all the materials we required, carried up here by the fishermen, and soon we got to work.

First we wanted to test the explosive, as it was some fifteen to twenty years old. We put some in a coffee tin, with a grenade for a detonator, and buried it in the sand, ran a wire to a safe distance and pulled. There was a bang, and sand shot into the air. We put charges into the large containers and tried one – what a bang – a crater on the beach you could put a car in! We constructed four, and put in some bottles half-filled with cooking oil (to get the right sound and feel of a full drum of cooking oil). Tang arranged with the fishermen to have them delivered, while we cleared up and left the island before the bombs arrived. These would be transferred to a third party for labelling and delivery, so as not to leave a trail back to us.

It was time for the three of us to take some leave, and it was granted for a week each, starting on Friday. This fitted in just right for the plans. I informed Susie, and asked her to tell the girls Sunshine and Chalky would meet with them. I had explained to Chalky and Sunshine that Susie and I were going up country, but they could stay with the girls.

The three of us got together each night for the next week. We joked with each other.

"Don't go into any places of ill-repute next week. Only go to Mount Faber, highest point on the island. I know the girls will fix something up for the week, wait and see," I said.

The weekend came, and we were off downtown with the speed of light. Susie was there with the other two. "We are all going to Penang tonight," said Susie. I have ordered rooms at a hotel for you two and the girls. Jake and I will be going to another hotel. I want us all out of Singapore – the goods are being delivered as we speak. I have hired two Mercedes – Tang will drive one, and one of our bodyguards will drive the other."

Sunshine said, "We didn't bring anything with us."

"We buy all you need tomorrow, OK?"

The lads nodded their agreement. Susie and I got into the car with Tang and the rest into the other car. It wasn't long before we crossed the causeway into Malaya. We travelled north into a very black stormy night. The rain was hammering down – the only lights to be seen were from oil lamps and cooking fires in the houses along the road.

We pulled in after many hours' driving into at a small hotel in Genting Highlands. The air was cooler and pleasant up here, and the rain had stopped. We checked in, got three rooms and ordered a meal, after which we retired.

The following day we continued our journey to Butterworth and caught the ferry to Georgetown on the island of Penang. Susie and I parted company with the other four, but arranged to meet for a meal later. Susie took me to a hotel overlooking the harbour. We had the penthouse suite on the top floor, this being the highest building around (six floors up). There was a balcony overlooking the harbour, and what a view! Our luggage arrived and Susie started to unpack.

"That's a fine pair of binoculars," I said, as I lifted them and went to the window, "Powerful too."

"Thought you'd like them, Jake, I got them for you."

"Thanks, Susie." I came over and kissed her, then went outside with my new toy. I could see to the mainland and watched ships, pleasure craft, and the busy harbour right below. When I turned round Susie was lying on the bed with her head hanging down, watching me upside down, with her long hair trailing on the floor. She was near naked, and eating a banana very seductively. I got the message, put down the binoculars and removed my clothes as I crossed the room. Later, Susie went into the shower. I lay there for ten minutes, then went to join her. She was already drying herself. I went into the shower and must have spent fifteen minutes there. I was still drying my hair as I entered the room, then I heard a rifle bolt slam shut. I stopped in my tracks. I was looking at Susie sitting on the bed, ten feet away, pointing a rifle at me. She put the weapon up slowly. I breathed a sigh of relief.

"What's this all about?"

"Something else I want you to do."

"I see." I picked up the rifle and opened the bolt. The magazine and chamber were empty – it was the rifle and scope I had used for the demonstration on the beach – now fitted with a silencer!

"Tang delivered it while you were in the shower."

"And what am I expected to do with this?"

"My father has learned that the boss of the gang we are having trouble with is sailing from Singapore to Penang, and is due tomorrow. I only learned of this just before we departed from Singapore."

"But you had enough time to plan this caper, and get this rifle ready."

"Jake, my father planned this, not me! The gang boss – he has to moor his boat just below us, about two hundred yards away. My father has ordered this: we must do as he has ordered, if not he could have both of us killed."

"I see, but I don't like this. Someone might see us, I could miss,"

"That is why my father got the silencer. You can test it on the marker buoys in the harbour. My father is going to pay fifteen thousand dollars into your account as soon as his enemy is dead – and that's on top of the payment for the bombs."

As it started to get dark, I listened to the traffic. "I don't think anyone will hear a silenced shot over this racket, let's give it a try."

We went out onto the balcony and lay down on the sun mat, so we could see the harbour through the railings. I spotted a plastic bottle about two hundred yards out, aimed and fired – right on target. The second round found its mark, and the bottle disappeared below the water. We went back into the room and hid the rifle (rolled up in a towel) under the mattress. We dressed to go out and then there was a knock on the door. Susie answered it.

Tang was grinning as he came into the room. "We did it. I hear news on radio there has been two explosions in the Jalan Basir area of Singapore." Susie was ecstatic, dancing around the room. I opened a beer and handed it to Tang, and had one myself.

"Jake, we did it, we did it!"

"OK, Susie, calm down! Let's get ready and go tell the others."

We were all in good form by the time we sat down to eat. The girls were chatting away in Chinese; we also chatted away and sank a few beers. I did not tell the lads about the latest development – I thought I would wait till after the event. We were pleased with everything and we enjoyed ourselves to the full. Chalky was chanting, "Money, money, money! I'm in the money!" We made arrangements to go diving next day. None of us had dived before – it sounded like fun.

After the diving expedition, Susie and I returned to our apartment very tired. I crashed onto the bed and almost fell asleep. Susie went out onto the balcony then back into the room shouting, "They are here!"

I shot upright and went for a look. "I see it! A big green and white motor cruiser with an open sundeck covered with a canvas canopy. Pass the binoculars, Susie. Is that him – the fat man sitting with the two girls?"

"That's him, Jake. Shall we do it now?"

"No, I need to rest first. Steady down." I went inside and lay on the bed. Susie lay beside me and we fell asleep. Some time later we both shot out of the bed. There was a thunderous explosion and the sky glowed in the darkness outside our room – everything was shaking like an earthquake. We ran to the balcony, and what a sight greeted us as we looked down. The dock area was a mass of burning wood and bits of boat scattered over a wide area. Some of it had set fire to other boats and cars on the waterfront. There was chaos down there. We looked at each other.

"Jake! That was the boat – what happened?"

"I don't know. Let me think – I'm confused." I went back in and sat down. "Susie, do you think your father managed to somehow get one of our bombs on board?"

"No, Jake. The bombs went to their premises."

"What if someone there – maybe the cook – took a drum or two of oil along with provisions for the sea trip?" We both looked at each other, and burst our sides laughing. "Let's find the others and get a drink – I need it!" I went back outside on the balcony to watch the fun.

"I just hope the fat man was on board," Susie said. We would soon know. We got ourselves ready and headed for the hotel where the others were already in the bar.

"Would you like a drink, you two?" said Chalky.

"Manners already – there's hope for us yet! Of course we would."

Before we could sit down, Sunshine asked if we'd heard about an explosion in the harbour.

"Yes," I said. "We saw – it a right bloody mess!"

"The news said it was some gangland boss and his crew who had arrived from Singapore. All dead," said Chalky. "Messy business."

I laughed and I saw Susie grinning. I just had to tell them my thoughts. The grinning turned to laughter as it sunk in. "Must've been something the fat bastard had for his evening meal!" said Sunshine. We laughed till the tears rolled. Susie couldn't have wished for a better outcome to the day.

We decided to leave the area and spent the rest of our leave in the Cameron Highlands. Before the week was out there had been another explosion in Singapore.

Chapter 7

Confrontation

It was May 1963 and time to return to Borneo to start long range patrolling of the Indonesian Border, and to train tribesmen as Border Scouts. This wasn't easy, as the border was eight hundred miles of undefined mountains, thick with jungle. The Battalion was going to be thin on the ground and risks were going to be high, unless more troops could be brought out here from the UK. There were already cross-border raids by Indonesia, so it was up to the Queen's Own Highlanders and our Gurkha friends to spearhead the British operation.

The three battalions arrived in Brunei and were quickly deployed to set up base camps close to the border, and to start patrolling the areas around them. Chalky was sent to an area of Sarawak, while Sunshine and I went back to Tawau, at the eastern end of the border.

The patrols were long – mostly of a week to ten days' duration. Most of our finds amounted to illegal immigrants and information from locals. Some of the headhunting tribes were operating over the border, collecting heads for the British and getting paid for it. This had the effect of making the Indonesians nervous about crossing the border until more troops were deployed. On one such patrol I was stung in the eye by a hornet – a big, dirty black one. I was to spend a few weeks getting my sight back in that eye.

On another patrol we found an old railway track that led to a banana plantation, and discovered it was built by prisoners of war for the Japanese. The workers here were from the islands to the south of the Philippines, and very friendly. We collected much information about communist cells recruiting in this area. Not many miles from there, we found four graves: one was marked with the remains of a wooden cross. The name was no longer there, but it was made from an army ammo box with Australian markings. The following week we found more rail lines and an engine with a boxcar, in an area of unexplored jungle known as the Gap. The rail line was only long enough for the engine to stand on, and the whole thing was overgrown by the jungle.

"I think the lines have been removed from front and rear and then used at another location," said the Platoon Commander. There was no other explanation.

We built our bashers for the night alongside the old boxcar. It was getting dark when I went just five yards outside the camp area with my trenching tool and toilet paper in hand, along with rifle and belt kit that never left my side. I had tied a string to the first bush so as not to get lost – some people had got lost and disoriented a few yards from base camp. I was squatting in the bush, listening to the night noise of crickets, fruit bats and monkeys, my trousers down and just comfortable, when the ground moved. I fell into a hole and rolled down a slope, coming to rest against what felt like a box. I struggled to my feet and pulled up my trousers, fumbling around in the dark for my webbing – fortunately my rifle was still in my hand. I didn't yell out, as I had no idea what had happened. I found my torch, switched it on, shading the light, and looked around.

There were boxes – old ammo boxes, about a dozen with Jap markings. I was in a small cave, or maybe it was a dugout! I went further in. It narrowed to about four feet then opened into a large steel-plated tank. The wall panels were bolted together like a water tank, the roof about eight feet high. Some of the area was caved in, with tree roots down to ground level and the place stank of decay and rotting vegetation.

There seemed to be a lot of boxes, some piled six feet high, other items covered with canvas. I was becoming spooked as I stood there in one spot, shining my torch around. I started to back out: this could be a hiding place or camp for bandits, although it appeared that no one had been in here for years. I found my way back and climbed out with some difficulty. I was only five yards from the rest of the lads, but I was careful to find my string and follow it back the way I came. I got back to my basher, and Sunshine was sitting by a fire with a brew going. The rest of the lads were doing the same, and I could smell curry.

"Took you a long time to have a dump!"

"Been saving it up for a week," I replied, as I sat down. "Let's get the curry on while I tell you what I have found."

Sunshine looked at me. "Don't tell me, there's a night club through the trees, there!"

"No, nothing like that; is the Platoon Commander around?"

"Young Sir is up at the front end of the engine, why?"

"I found a cave with ammo boxes. I fell into it while I was having a dump."

"You would fall in the shit and come up smelling of roses! Is this a lot of bullshit?" said Sunshine.

"No. When everyone settles down we'll go back in."

"We could get lost. You can't see your hand in front of your face."

"Sunshine, stop worrying, I know the way in. I used para cord tied to the first bush here, and it goes all the way to the hole – no problem."

"We're going to tell the boss, Jake?"

"Not till we check it out." We finish the curry and lie back to wait.

By 2000 hours all was quiet, and we slipped away unnoticed: armed with rifle, torch, one trenching tool, para cord and a candle each. I retraced my steps and dropped down into the hole. I still had plenty of cord to continue on past the first boxes and enter the bunker. We lit two candles and placed them on both sides of the doorway, on tree roots, and turned our torches on. Now we could see the size of the place, which was about twenty feet wide by fifty feet long. There were rusty steel supports for the roof at intervals. We could see another doorway at the far end.

I noticed the surprise on Sunshine's face as he looked around. "Jake, I though you were joking. This looks like a workshop – look, that's a blacksmith's forge and there are railway fittings – must have been something to do with that engine out there."

"Sunshine, look over here: this looks like humans – three skeletons! A British web belt, look at these two!" They had on army boots, what was left of them, no dog tags.

"Jake, look at this: all three have had their skulls smashed in at the back. Better report this, Jake."

I was by now thinking the same as I approached the first pile of boxes: all wood and in not bad condition, with lids screwed down. We used the trenching tool to force open lids. Once open, there was waxed paper with Japanese writing on it. I tore it away and we were looking at bullets all in mint condition. "Bloody hell, let's try some more," I said, and we proceeded to another pile of boxes. "These look like rifle boxes." There were bolt-action rifles, and stick grenades. "Yes, we'd better report this," I said as I pulled a canvas cover off some ammo boxes, and nearly choked on the dust. "Let's try one more before we go." As the lid came off we froze to the spot, looked at each other then back at the box.

"Bloody hell – gold bars!" said Sunshine, as we bent down to examine our find. We emptied the box – ten bars.

"Now what the hell are we going to do?" I said.

"Try another one, Jake?" Sunshine was already working on the next box. It was the same. We sat and looked at the gold for a while, thinking what to do.

"Oh God, we're in deep shit now. We can't tell anyone," I said. We put the lids back on, and the canvas over the boxes. "We can't tell anyone about this and we can't take any with us." We sat on a box and worked out what to do. "We know the area we're in – all we need to do is find our way back to the engine at a later date."

"But how do the locals not know anything about the engine? This is supposed to be an unexplored area known as The Gap. No one has ever ventured into this area, so we are told."

"Look, we know we're going to the river tomorrow, and it's about a one hour march on a compass bearing that we don't know! We need that bearing; then we make a back-bearing from the point we emerge on the river bank. That's the place we must mark and remember."

"Then what, Jake? We aren't going to get the chance to come back here – never!"

"If the officers get to know about this we get shit anyway. When we get back to Singapore we tell Susie and she'll fix it."

"Let's take one each, Jake."

"What are we going to do with it – carry it all over Borneo? After this op we return to Singapore. How do we get it through Customs and kit checks? Better we leave it here."

"Let's get back. We have been in here over two hours. Hope no one is looking for us."

"When we get to the end of the cord I'll detach it, we crawl back to our basher, then I'll pull in the cord."

All was quiet as we crawled into our basher. We lay there not sleeping as we were still on a high, trying to comprehend what we'd found, and feeling rather sick that we couldn't take a bar or two with us.

We waited until just before first light, got the brew on and some scoff down our necks and prepared to move out. The Rupert was looking at his map, or rather an aerial photo of the area.

I went over. "What's our location Sir?"

"Don't really know," came the reply, "I think about here." He pointed with a pencil – the only thing marked was the village we stayed at more than a week ago, and many miles away – the rest was all grey photo, with what looked like a river running across it.

"How do we get out of here, Sir?"

"Bearing of 225 degrees and we hit the river, but I don't know where." I had the information I needed. Then Rupert decided he was going to explore forward and to the rear of the engine, for two hundred yards, to see if there was any more rail track. Sunshine and I parked our kit and sat on it, barring the approach to the entrance of the hole that was well overgrown, considering how I managed to find it in the dark. The Rupert went off with four men and soon returned, having found no more rails – then off the other way, also finding nothing. Meanwhile, I took my trenching tool and headed into the bush, back to the dugout. Anyone watching would take it for granted I was going for a dump. Sunshine covered the way I went. I saw the hole for the first time in daylight. It didn't take much to camouflage the entrance. The hole wasn't as big as it felt in the dark and there was plenty of foliage around it.

The Rupert returned and we set off for the river. I only had a button compass in the handle of my knife. It had no bearing marks, only points of the compass, but it was good enough. We reached the river just after midday, and our signaller tapped off a message in Morse code requesting a patrol boat to pick us up. The radio operator jotted down the message and handed it to the Rupert. The message read: *'Stay put ... stop. Patrol boat at 1400 hours tomorrow... stop. Out.'*

We moved back from the river's edge, bashered up for the night and placed guards on the river banks. An army Beaver spotter plane flew over us at first light and a short while later a radio message was received: *'Enemy active in your area ... stop. Canoes, five, seen ten miles up river from your position at 1045 hours ... stop. If opportunity should arise, engage enemy ... stop. Reinforcement on way, estimated time of arrival 1400 ... stop. Out.'*

"Here we go again, hold till relieved; eight of us against the whole Indo army."

"Better sharpen the bayonet, Jake, and those two knives you carry! I don't think we're going to get out of this one."

"Sunshine, we have to get back to Singapore – we've got a lot to see to, right?"

"Roger that, Jake!"

The Rupert was running around, flapping. "Two over there with a Bren, two over here with the other Bren, two riflemen in the middle here. I will be behind with the radio operator over here. Nobody opens fire until I give the word."

"Sunshine, have you noticed we are on the only sandy beach area along this part of the river as far as we can see?"

"What are you getting at, Jake?"

"If, and only if, the Indos were to come ashore, it would be on the beach – and there's always the unthinkable possibility it could be this one."

"Are you going to tell him, Jake?"

"No, it's too late – here come the first two canoes."

"Shit!"

We marked our targets. My finger was on the trigger, safety off. The first boat was now level with us, then the second, and then they were going out of sight round a bend from us. A third boat appeared and went past.

"What the hell is going on?" I looked over my shoulder to the Rupert's trench. No Rupert! I got the attention of the radio operator – he was pointing to the rear and mouthing, "Having a dump."

I looked back at the river, and there were numbers four and five – about eight men in each canoe – just about level with us. I fired and shouted, "Fire! Do the bastards!" All hell broke loose. The boats rolled over, splintering, as the soldiers went down like ninepins; three still alive, being carried along by the current. "Shoot them!" I shouted, and saw them disappear below the water in a hail of fire, as the lads got to their feet and raced to the water's edge, pumping out lead at a hell of a rate. The Rupert came running out of the undergrowth, trying to dress himself, and shouting his head off.

"I bet that gave him the runs," I said.

"What the hell is going on, who told you to fire? I gave no orders. No one was to fire till I said so. What happened?" Then two shots rang out from the far bank. The Rupert was first to hit the deck – the quickest time ever! Sunshine had spotted the sniper on the far bank, and put him down with one shot. The Indo fell back into the river.

"Must have been a survivor from one of the canoes – the other three canoes went down the river, round the bend. We'd better move our position back into the jungle a few hundred yards, in case they've landed and are coming this way to see what all the noise is about."

"Yes, that's a jolly good idea. Let's move."

We followed the Rupert and stopped after a few hundred yards. We went into 'all round defence', sat in the bush for three hours and heard nothing. Signals had managed to send a report of the contact. Some hours later we returned to the beach, got a brew on and waited for the reinforcements to arrive. Sunshine and I went to work marking and remembering every detail of this beach. We gathered all the ration tins and any rubbish, burying it in front of a predominant tree. I got a length of signal cable and tied it around a branch – this would last for years unless someone found it and removed it. We built a small cairn behind the tree.

Late afternoon, our helicopters arrived with Gurkhas. We were informed that more Gurkhas had found the canoes down river, and were now in pursuit of the enemy. We were now to return on the choppers as the river patrol had been abandoned.

We landed back at Tawau, and just had enough time to pack our kit and get on flights back to Brunei to regroup with the rest of the Battalion. We arrived and found we were in a tented camp. We soon found a tent fit for our gang. Platoons were returning from the border area by the hour. We were seeing old friends, and it wasn't long till I ran into Chalky and had a quick exchange of notes. The three of us met up in the beer tent that night.

Chalky said, "I've been talking to some SAS lads and it looks like they're going to be operating here for a long time. They are looking for people, and I think I'll go for selection."

"What's that, Chalky?" I asked. So Chalky told us all he knew: fitness, hill-walking, map reading, navigating, ending in forty miles (twenty-four hours with full rucksack) up in the Welsh mountains!

"I think we can handle that after all we've been through here."

"Well, I don't want the bullshit we're going to get when we arrive in Germany, and I'd sooner be here."

"Me too," said Sunshine. "Count me in."

"Can't refuse this one. If they do, I've got a number to phone," said Chalky.

"We'd better not all try to go at the same time – the management will get upset." Although we didn't really know what was involved, information on the SAS was kept top secret.

We told Chalky about our find. It was hard work trying to convince him we weren't joking, but we eventually succeeded by the time we reached Singapore.

Cpl. Tustin with border scouts
All issued with uniforms but will not use boots

Cpl. Tustin Queens Own Highlanders
training Border Scouts

Some of our Gurkha friends

Sgt. J.J. Lewis and Bill Andrews doing a little wine tasting

Munro 49 dancing the night away in a Longhouse after much rice wine

Chapter 8

Who Cares Anyway

We couldn't wait to get downtown and see the girls. As soon as we sorted our gear and had a good clean up, we were off as fast as we could.

The arrangement was to meet the girls at the usual spot, and we didn't have to wait long before Tang pulled up and the girls appeared, looking stunning in their cheongsams of very colourful silk – their make-up done to perfection.

"Hi girls, let's go eat," said Sunshine. "I'm starved. Hawker stall sound good?"

"No boys. After what you have been through, we hear on radio, so tonight we dine at Orchard Hotel, and I'm paying," said Susie. We trooped into the Orchard Hotel and were shown to a table.

"Bit posh," said Sunshine as he sat down, confronted with more swords and daggers than he had ever seen before.

"Different from a spoon and mess tin," said Chalky, laughing. We felt we had arrived back in heaven.

The girls had not yet been complimented so I did the honours, to the amusement of Chalky and Sunshine. We ordered drinks and the biggest steaks on the menu. The girls could not get over the sheer amount of food we were packing away, and by the time we'd finished we were like poisoned pups.

After the meal we retired to the bar. Susie struck up the conversation. "There has been some trouble here with the gang you just about put out of business. The son of fat man, who was killed on the boat in Penang harbour, is running the gang now. They fire bombed four of our premises. Twelve people died, including three of our staff."

"Is your father not happy with our work, Susie?"

"Jake, he is more than happy with the help he had from all of you. What has happened is not your fault, but we have to be careful. We are known to this gang, and anyone with us will be targeted also." We looked at each other, and nodded our understanding. "I noticed Tang in the yellow car on our way in – best get him another car, a black one."

Susie looked at the three of us. She got the message. "I'll take care of it," she said.

Chalky and Ruby decided to order a taxi and go on ahead; we got another round of drinks in to pass the time. Then Mai Ling went to reception and ordered a taxi for herself and Sunshine. Susie and I would go last with Tang. The taxi arrived and Sunshine and Mai Ling left us at the bar. About five minutes passed then Mai Ling reappeared with Sunshine following, looking over his shoulder. Mai Ling was talking in Chinese to Susie, at a rate of knots, and the tears were flowing. I knew something was far wrong. "Sunshine, what in the hell is going on?"

"When we walked out of the hotel, we thought there was a riot going on. Then we noticed the yellow car – it was Tang – his throat cut!"

"Oh shit, it's started and us on our first night out. What now?" I said. We sat at a table in the corner of the bar – Sunshine and I sitting with our backs to the wall, instinctively. We were aware of the attention other customers were giving us.

"I have to make a phone call," said Susie, getting up and heading for the phones by reception. I went along too as extra eyes. When we returned, I could see Mai Ling was going into shock. Sunshine had already called for the hotel doctor, who was there very quickly and attended to Mai Ling.

"Father is very angry, but is sending cars and help for us. They will be here soon."

Time seemed to drag as we waited, our brains racing in anticipation – what happens next? Then one of the minders walked into the bar – I recognised him. Words were exchanged. We stood up and all headed for the door, as Susie chatted to the minder. The yellow car had gone and everyone had dispersed as if nothing had happened. That's how it is in this part of the world. We were going to miss Tang badly. There were two minibuses waiting, both with blacked out windows, and the side door of the first vehicle opened as we approached. We climbed in, and were met by one of the minders sitting with a Thompson sub-machine gun on his lap. We moved off, with the second vehicle following close behind. Not a word was spoken until we reached the house.

The house was a hive of activity as we entered: minders rushing from room to room with guns and maps, shouting instructions to each other. Sunshine was all eyes just looking the house over. Susie headed for the dining room and we followed. There were Chalky and Ruby sitting drinking tea. Mai Ling poured tea for the rest of us and passed the cups around. Susie was deep in thought, and I judged it best to keep my thoughts to myself at this time; I was going over all the events since I first met Susie.

I remembered back to one day when Susie and I were doing the rounds and visited a boarding house, run by two Indian brothers, down by the Singapore River. It was a two storey building of colonial design, with a small attractive garden and a fountain in the middle of the driveway. Tang parked the car outside on the road, and Susie and I got out and went through the iron gates and up to the front door – which looked very solid, heavy wood, with iron fittings of Asian design. I banged the knocker twice. There was an echo from within, and the door was opened by a house girl who was dressed in traditional black pyjamas. We were shown into the hallway – it had polished wood panels, with a black and white tiled floor. There was just one table at the far end, with a door each side. The girl disappeared through the left one then one of the brothers appeared. He raised his voice and started shouting at Susie in English, before she said a word, with his arms flying about and plenty of choice words. My hands were in my pockets on my knives. Then Susie turned slowly and nodded to me. I got the drift as I noticed the Indian put his hand into his jacket and pull out a revolver. Susie had turned her back to him as I threw my first knife underhand, sticking him in the throat. He dropped the revolver and fell to his knees, as I shot forward and stuck him again in the chest with my second knife. It all happened so fast, and instinctively. By the time I removed the knives he was dead: his blood was all over the tiled floor and spreading rapidly over the polished black and white tiles.

We left in a hurry, and could hear the screams of the house girl as we told Tang to give the car the boot. Susie was furious, as she thanked me for my fast reaction, and vowed revenge on the Indian family for the insults and loss of face in front of a Westerner. Loss of face was more important to her than the money, but she would sort that.

Back at the house, Susie asked me to wait in her room as she handed me the key. She was already talking to some of the minders as they entered her father's office, and the door shut behind her. I was not yet privy to all that went on – I would not ask – best to hear all and say nothing. I opened the door to Susie's room and went out onto the balcony with my own thoughts, put my feet up and watched the sun set. I nodded off, and was awakened by Mai Ling touching my left ear.

"Hi, Jake, you OK? I hear you have busy day today, we go and eat now. Susie is waiting in the dining room." We chatted as we made our way downstairs.

In the dining room, Susie was beaming and looking happy again. I was wondering if the other brother was now having his nuts cut off by Susie's minders.

"Business all sorted," she said. "Come and eat."

Sunshine and Chalky were certainly enjoying themselves. The new girlfriends were paying much attention to them, and they were lapping it up.

Several weeks were to pass before I found out what reprisals had taken place. I picked up little snippets of conversation between Susie, Mai Ling and Tang, and also a story I read in the local newspaper – about two Indian teenage sisters being kidnapped from the address in Singapore, and a ransom being demanded. Then I overheard Tang saying something about the two Indian girls working in one of the brothels in Penang owned by Susie's father. It looked like the ransom had not been paid and this was the way to get the money.

The door to the dining room opened, and I jerked back into real time as we stood up. It was the big boss himself. The girls greeted him and introduced Chalky and Sunshine. He sat at the head of the table and indicated for us to sit down. He opened with an apology for us getting caught up in their troubles then thanked us for our past assistance.

"I intend to strike back quickly. At this moment my men are getting ready. We strike tonight."

I butted in, "Sir, I think there is a better way."

He looked at me, "Please speak, Mr Jake." Oh shit! The plan was only half-formed in my mind. The other half would develop once I started talking – I hoped.

"Sir, the enemy knows to expect an attack or reprisals from you, but they don't know us three yet." I looked at Sunshine and Chalky. "Sir, for my part in this, I am willing to take the fight to your enemy, and I will cause devastation in one of their premises. I will have only one attempt at it – there is no second chance."

"Yes, there is," said Chalky. "Count me in!"

"Me too," said Sunshine. This way we could hit three places at the same time.

"Gentlemen, please. This is not your fight, why get involved? I have never understood the British."

"We like to fight, explained Chalky. It's what we do best, and this is just a good laugh and some excitement for us. Anyway, you can hit them again later."

The boss sat there, tapping the table, deep in thought then started to laugh. "OK, gentlemen. Make a plan and give it to Susie for my approval. Just ask for anything you need." We stood up. As he took his leave, he said, "You will be well rewarded for your efforts, gentlemen."

"Well lads, we were never called gentlemen before. We best get started." We followed Susie into the hall, while Mai Ling and Ruby remained in the dining room. We entered the money room – it was deserted, and made our way down the stairs to the basement, with its low wattage bulb showing the mess of dirty boxes and old junk.

Sunshine said, "What are we doing down here, and what's happening?" Chalky was looking around bewildered, then the sound of the wall moving started. "What's that noise, Jake?"

The wall started to move as Susie came down the stairs. I wanted to see their faces when the lights came on. We stared into the dark, and then the lights flickered on. The lads were open-mouthed at the sight before them.

"Bloody hell!" They had big grins as we went into the armoury. "Look at this! Look at that!" It was every boy's dream come true; they could not believe their eyes. I was still having trouble believing my own.

"Come over here, lads. Look at this timer device fitted to an adjustable web strap. I don't know what it was intended for, but it will fit round a grenade, holding down the lever after the pin has been pulled. The timer can be set for two minutes or two hours – watch this." I set the timer for two minutes, and as we watched the time indicator count down to zero there was a click and the fastening came apart. I then took a grenade and removed the base plug to check there was no detonator; then fitted the strap, pulled it tight, removed the pin from the grenade, set the timer for two minutes and waited for zero. Soon as the strap was released, the lever flew off and the striker shot out of the base hole. "Take one each and test them out." I then took a phosphorus grenade. "This is what we will use – we put one each in a bum bag around our middle, like usual. No one will notice anything odd. It did not take us more than five minutes to get three grenades ready, so we wasted time messing around with all the weapons till Susie returned with three bum bags.

Work over, we decided to go swimming on Sentosa then on to Mount Faber for lunch. We returned to the house in the minibus, in time to see the back door of the minibus being shut, but not before we saw bodies and blood in the back.

"What's going on, Susie?"

"I find out. You three go with the girls to the dining room."

"Lovely company you keep, Jake," said Chalky, joking.

"Makes you feel at home!" said Sunshine.

We waited, and Susie returned ten minutes later and sat at the head of the table. "Some of our men found five of the other gang, took them for a drive and killed them."

"Bloody hell!" said Sunshine. "How are you going to get rid of them?"

"No problem. We deliver them tonight to the crocodile farm."

Chalky burst out laughing. "Bloody outrageous! I can just see Glasgow with a croc farm!" The three of us burst out laughing but Susie didn't see what was funny, so I explained.

"Ah, now I understand. You are three very funny men."

"You very funny people too," said Sunshine, and we all laughed. Susie took us to the armoury to collect our presents for tonight, and showed us the selected targets. She organised a driver and minibus organised, and we went downtown to view our targets. Now we could relax for the rest of the day.

2000 hours. I was dropped by minibus near Bugis Junction, and the other two not far away. I bought a beer, sat at a hawker's stall and eyed the scene. It wasn't long until I was being approached by a pimp.

"Sir, you want short time, maybe all night?"

"No," I replied.

"Very nice girls, never been with man before, Sir, big discount on all night."

"I don't believe you."

"You come see, Sir. Plenty bargain, just over there. That place very good – no MPs." He was pointing right at the place I wanted.

"OK, I come with you – better be good!" We crossed the road and I entered the property. There was a lot of Chinese chit-chat going on as the girls were lined up for inspection. I picked out the best from the bunch, and the pimp was paid. The girl showed me to a room and we started to strip for action. I lay on the bed watching her strip, then she walked into the shower room and shut the door. I reached for the bum bag and put my hand inside, setting the timer for two hours, then removed it from the bag and rolled it under the bed, just as she came out of the shower room and jumped over me onto the bed. I gave her a good seeing-to in record time. I was hoping, against hope, the timer was working accurately or there was going to be a premature ejaculation! We finished and I dressed, picked up the bum bag, made my way downstairs and came face to face with the pimp.

"You have good time, Sir? She number one girl, very good, ha, ha!" He passed me on his way up the stairs to get his hard-earned dollars.

"You have a nice evening, friend!" I shouted after him, and made my way back to Bugis Junction. I waited for the minibus – it was right on time. There was Sunshine in the back, giving me the thumbs up, and I returned it as we headed for the next pick-up point. We got there – no Chalky! We waited for about half an hour, and were starting to get concerned in case an explosion happed before we got out of the area. Then the driver spotted Chalky heading our way at the double. We picked him up. "What happened to you?"

"The bitch wanted to come with me."

"You were that good? You must have made an impression," I said.

"Never knew you were that well equipped!" Sunshine added

"How did you get rid of her?" I asked.

"Gave her a Glasgow kiss, and left her around the corner there," he pointed. As we passed, I could see the figure of a girl slumped against a wall.

"What a way to treat a woman! Chalky, we're shocked that you would do such a thing!" Sunshine and I just grinned.

We got back to the house and reported to Susie. She was glad to see us all back without incident. "We just have to sit back and wait for the results now," I said.

"We best turn in now, it's late."

"Yes, Susie. At least an hour to go till the first fire I reckon. I've had enough excitement for one night," said Chalky.

We all retired for the night. Susie and I soaked in the bath and started to relax. "Susie, I haven't had time to tell you about our last trip to Borneo."

"Not now. I am very tired, Jake."

"Bet the crocodiles slept well after their feed today?" Still no response! "Would gold wake you up?"

Her eyes opened wide. "Did you say gold?"

"It's OK, Susie. If you're tired, I'll tell you tomorrow," I teased.

"Tell me now, Jake. Now I am awake!" So I told her the whole story. She was stunned. "We tell father tomorrow," she said. "He will know what to do."

The next morning we went down to breakfast and met the

others. Everyone was feeling better after a good night's sleep. I informed the others I had told Susie about our find. Mai Ling and Ruby looked puzzled, wondering what I was talking about, so Susie enlightened them.

"Not a word of this is to go beyond this room!" she ordered. When the food arrived and we got stuck in, Susie got up and left the room. We started joking about the night before and things were becoming silly, when the door opened and Susie and her father entered. We stood up.

"Good morning, gentlemen. I hope you slept well. Please sit and continue with your meal, as I speak. Susie has told me about your find, but first I want to congratulate you on a very successful operation last night. I can tell you all three bombs went off, and set fire to the properties. I don't know about casualties yet. There was much damage, and the police have closed the area until an investigation can be carried out."

"Now, about this gold: I have heard much about gold hidden by the Japanese General Yamashita. I met him here in Singapore during the occupation – a very evil man. They say the gold is hidden in sites throughout the Philippines. I never heard of any being in Borneo. This is very interesting, Jake. Can you tell me the location? I think we could recover it."

"Sir, as much as we would like to recover this gold we cannot get to it, as the area is a war zone and very active." I explained our position: the area of the bunker, the enemy incursions into the area, and the fact no one would find the bunker without Sunshine or me.

"OK, Jake, now I understand. We wait for the war to finish, and then we go."

"That's the only way, Sir. I don't know if Susie has told you yet – we're going home to Scotland in three months' time, but all three of us will return before long."

"Yes, she told me, but first you will have a very good Christmas, and go home with money in your bank accounts. Excuse me now, gentlemen, but I have much to do."

We returned to our duties at Changi, and the three of us had no time off for the next three weeks – what with guard duties and fire pickets, along with training and general bullshit that goes on. We met together some nights for a few pints of Tiger and a chat and picked up some news on the radio about gang warfare downtown, but no indication as to who, why or what. Our chance came to get out of camp, and we made arrangements to meet the girls in the bar at Raffles. Orchard Hotel had now become a no-go area for us, as we didn't know who was watching since the killing of Tang.

The girls were in the bar when we got there, and couldn't wait to tell us what had been going on. As I was getting the drinks in, Chalky and Sunshine were all ears as Mai Ling told of how she and Susie went to a shop to collect money. One of the drivers was outside in the car, waiting for the girls. "Susie was expecting trouble with the couple who own that shop, as we know their son is working with our old rivals. They refused to pay their dues, so Susie turned to leave – they shouted at her, thinking they had the upper hand. I was standing at the door with a beach bag, with the machine gun inside. Susie reached into the bag, took out the gun, turned round and shot all three of them dead, using all the bullets. Bang, bang, bang! She didn't stop till the gun was empty, then dropped it on the floor and we ran out to the car and left. What a noise – what a mess!"

"Susie, is this right?" I asked.

"Yes, Jake. I had to do it or lose face."

"I told you before to let the men do the collections."

"I know, but my father said long ago there would be less trouble if Mai Ling and I did the collections."

"But things have changed over the last few months, and you

will have to change along with them if you want to stay in business,"
I said.

"Jake, my father ordered the men to fire bomb and shoot any of
our rivals, and they have been busy over the last three weeks. People
have died on both sides. The police have not been involved – I think
they are happy to let the gangs fight to a standstill."

"You're probably right, Susie. Then they have only one gang to
deal with."

"If that is so, Jake, we will buy off the police later!"

"Let's change the subject," said Sunshine. "How about we head to
Bedok Corner for some seafood?" We all agreed, ordered two cars
with minders, and off we went.

We sat outside as there was a gentle breeze coming off the sea, and
it was always busy here – so less likely to attract trouble. We ate and
drank the night away, had a good laugh, then got back into the cars
and went back downtown to Raffles for a drink till midnight. We had
arranged for the minibus to collect us from a pre-arranged point. We
found the minibus driver fast asleep, but he soon moved when Susie
banged on the door. We all climbed in, and it wasn't long before we
were at the house and heading for the bedrooms. The house seemed
quiet these days.

"Susie, are there any customers in?"

"Yes, there should be. But we have been very careful who comes
here – only our best clients. We have a look." She headed for the TV
room, and was soon flicking the camera from room to room. Most
rooms had someone in, but not much action; so I put my arms round
Susie and squeezed at the same time, switching off the TV, and
pulling her back into the bedroom.

In the morning, at breakfast, I suggested to Susie that all the arms
they had should be disposed of or sold, as they were well out of
date. "There's a market with the Burmese hill people fighting for

independence. Even stash the arms up in the north around the islands of Langkawi, up in the north-west. If I know your father, it won't be long before he gets his hands on new guns from Vietnam."

"I will tell him what you say."

"We'd better be getting back to camp," said Chalky.

"Yes, we must, but we'll see you on Tuesday night, if that's all right?" I said, as the three of us weren't going to be on duty.

Mai Ling nodded, and Susie said, "OK, we meet at Cathay Cinema, six-thirty. Ruby, go and ask for the minibus to take the boys back to Changi." We said our goodbyes and boarded the minibus. We were dropped in Changi village and went back to camp by taxi.

Tuesday arrived, and we took a taxi into town. Chalky broke the news that he had put in his application for selection for the SAS. "How long is it going to take to process?" asked Sunshine.

"Only a couple of weeks. There are only three courses a year, so I hope to be on the summer one. We'll be back in the UK before that."

"I'll get mine in next month," said Sunshine.

"I suppose I'd better wait until we get back to the UK," I said.

We arrive at the Cathay Cinema, paid the taxi driver, and went to have a look what was on, as we were early. Six-thirty came and went, and we started to get concerned. Then I saw the moneyman and a minder heading in our direction, looking very frightened and pale.

"Jake, you come!" I asked what was wrong, but I couldn't understand Chinese, and this man and the minder didn't speak English. "Come on, lads let's go with him." We followed.

The minibus was round the corner with the engine running. We got in the back and headed off in the direction of the house. The house came into sight. As we drove up the drive there seemed to be a lot of activity. We left and went into the hall – the women were weeping. Then Mai Ling came out of one of the rooms, also weeping. We approached her, and all at the same time, asked, "What happened?"

"It is very bad. Susie and Ruby are dead."

"How?"

"Both shot this afternoon on the way to meet you. After being dropped off downtown, they went shopping first and that was when it happened."

"Where are they now, Mai Ling?"

"The police have the bodies." All three of us put our arms around her.

"Oh, Christ," said Sunshine.

"Is your father here?" I asked.

"No, but he is coming, Jake."

"Mai Ling, you are number one girl now. Be strong for your father. We'll miss them both very badly, but we must go from here now. We can't get involved further in this. Please pass on our condolences to your father. We'll be in touch soon, but now we must go and think." We walked down the drive, turned right, and headed down the street till we joined the main road, where we found a taxi.

"Changi village," Chalky said, as we got in. There was much to think about, and much we wanted to say to each other, but not within earshot of the taxi driver.

At Changi, we went to the bar and got in the beers. All three of us had tears in our eyes. "Think we did the right thing, lads, getting out of there?"

"Jake, I think we've stuck our necks out far enough," said Chalky.

"It's a shame about the girls – but this could end no other way, the way they were going," said Sunshine.

"We can't go near the funerals even if we wanted to! It will be a big Chinese affair, everyone beating gongs and barking at the moon."

"Let's leave it a week or two then I'll make contact with Mai Ling. We've the business of the gold to think about. Sunshine and I are the only two who know how to get to it."

The three of us were reduced to drinking and fighting in the Brit club.

The talk in camp was all about our coming move to the UK, then on to Germany. I decided to phone Mai Ling and meet her at the bar in Changi. We met one evening, and I was surprised to see her smiling face. It was as if I was looking at Susie as she came over to me, with her arms outstretched. "Jake, nice to see you. Are you well?"

"Yes I'm well, Mai Ling. How are you?" I kissed her on the cheek. To look at her, one wouldn't have thought anything had happened. "Let's sit over here and you can tell me your news." I ordered some drinks.

"Jake, you and your friends did all you could, and did the right thing not getting involved further."

"I wish we could've done more. How is your father?"

"He is well, but he ordered revenge on those who killed my sister and Ruby. He is also moving all the arms up north, as you advised."

"You know I must return to the UK soon?"

"Yes, Jake, I know, and we must have a night out before you go; Sunshine and Chalky too. Are they in camp?"

"Yes, Mai Ling. They don't know I'm here. I didn't want too much pressure on you, until I found out how everything is with you."

"Jake, we all have to move on – the dead are dead, and all we have is memories. Call me to arrange our night out. Now I must return home." She entered a waiting car and waved as it drove off.

The next two weeks passed quickly. One night, Chalky and I went to the Cameron bar, a few miles down Changi road. Sunshine was there with friends from Edinburgh. Chalky and I returned to camp around ten-thirty, and were met with the news that Sunshine was dead – killed right outside the camp. Chalky and I took off for the site of the incident. Some of the lads were still there, and told of a hit and run driver – how the car hit him and dragged him to his death. "The RAF ambulance came and took him to RAF Changi camp hospital."

"Are you sure he was dead?" we asked. They were sure. Then we, along with most of the Battalion, went into Changi village and sat around until we had confirmation from RAF police. We all headed for camp, very sad, and with our own thoughts.

"Chalky, do you think this was an unfortunate accident, or something more sinister?"

"What are you getting at, Jake?

"Well, it occurs to me that we've been based in Singapore for three years, the Battalion's been through much, and Sunshine's the only loss!"

"Maybe he just stepped out into the road, Jake?"

"But then why didn't the driver stop? Do you think he was targeted?"

"Jake, we may never know. We've lost him and that's that, sad as it is."

The regiment buried Sunshine in Singapore, August of 1964. After the funeral, I phoned Mai Ling and told her what happened. I arranged for Chalky and I to meet her for that night out. We met at Raffles, and Mai Ling brought along a girl called Helen as company for Chalky. We had a drink for Sunshine. Mai Ling was thinking the same as I, but there was no proof so far. We had a very entertaining evening, and at the end of the night Chalky went off somewhere with Helen, and Mai Ling and I spent the night in Raffles. It was to be the last time I saw Mai Ling before returning to the UK.

Our training was intensive as we prepared for the return to the UK and then Germany. We moved down to RAF Changi and started boarding aircraft for the journey home. This was a big airlift – the first of its kind – as the troopships had ceased to operate the previous year. As I boarded the flight, I took a last look over my shoulder at the sun setting over the South China Sea, and thought of Sunshine.

We arrived at Turnhouse, Edinburgh, on a very cold winter's morning, with snow blowing in from the North Sea. We all had ten weeks' leave before reporting to Milton Bridge camp, south of

Edinburgh. I met up with Chalky, and he told me he was off on the next selection course in a week's time. I told him that I'd just put in my request and should be on the following selection course, but first I was going with the advance party to Germany on a mountain warfare course: escape and evasion, with the German army in Bavaria! We arranged to meet in Hereford when I arrived on selection, if Chalky was still in the UK that is.

We had a few nights out in Edinburgh before we parted company and went our separate ways. Little did I know it was to be the last time I was to see Chalky.

The course in Bavaria went well. I enjoyed it, and it prepared me for selection. I arrived back at the Battalion in Osnabruck to the news that Chalky had been killed in action in Borneo on his first operation with 22 SAS. It was like a hammer-blow to me – I couldn't believe it – it was like there was a curse on the three of us or something. Chalky was buried next to Sunshine in Singapore.

My turn came for selection, and I arrived in Hereford along with another one hundred and thirty other hopefuls. I recognised some lads from years before – old hands from my early days at Infantry Junior Leaders, Battalion Oswestry and Plymouth. It was like my first day at Junior Leaders – and that felt a long time ago. It was summer and I thought it would be fine on the hills, but it was the old Welsh weather treatment: rain, fog, and more rain!

Selection was an experience I will never forget, and an achievement that was hard-earned and rewarding. After just a few weeks, we were down to eight out of the hundred and thirty starters. I completed my training and remained with the Regiment until 1969, when my service ended.

Chapter 9

Ghosts from the Past

I awoke from my sleep, with Singapore girl touching my hand and saying, "Breakfast menu, Sir." I was jerked back to my surroundings and reality. People were moving about the aircraft organizing themselves for the day. Business man, next to me, was looking at his menu. I did the same, and Singapore girl came and took our orders. After breakfast I cleaned up and made myself ready for our arrival at Singapore Changi Airport – now said to be the best in the world!

Business man started talking about his wife and kids waiting for him at home. He asked if I was going into town, and said he could give me a lift as he had a car waiting for him. I accepted his offer and said I was going to the Lion City Hotel. We landed and entered the terminal. It was amazing – nothing like the Changi airport I remembered from so long ago.

I was dropped off at the Lion City Hotel, and thanked business man for the lift. The hotel was cool and comfortable; I wanted to rest and plan what to do from here on. I thought of times gone by – Susie, Mai Ling, Ruby, Tang, Sunshine and Chalky – and wondered if anything was as it had been –the big house (and centre of so much action). I went down to the lobby and ordered coffee and a taxi.

I asked the taxi driver to take me to the Military Cemetery at Kranji. I viewed the scenery and was amazed at the changes everywhere, as we proceeded north and arrived at the gate to Kranji late in the afternoon; it was still very hot.

I found both Sunshine and Chalky registered in the book at the gatehouse, and went to the gravesides to pay my respects, placing a thistle on the grave of each of my friends. I took some soil from the graves and put it into a small plastic container to take back to

Scotland. It was there I thought again about the past, and made up my mind to find the old house.

I returned to the hotel and had my evening meal, and retired early as the jet lag was catching up with me. Next day I was up bright and early, and took a taxi to drop me near the old house. I found it easily – it looked just like when I last saw it. Now there was a sign outside saying guest house. Very nervously, and with some apprehension, I approached the front door. So many thoughts were going through my head. It was like returning to the scene of a crime. My hand was shaking as I reached for the doorbell and rang twice. I stood there, looking at the old coach lamps, then the door opened, and there was Mai Ling – older, eyes bright and full of life, still very elegant and looking well for all the years. I couldn't believe it! I removed my baseball cap and sunglasses, and she started to cry.

"Is that you, Jake?" she said, looking hard into my face.

"Yes, it's me, Mai Ling – don't cry, or I will go away again!" I joked.

"Jake, I'm overjoyed to see you! Come in, come in." I lifted my backpack and walked through the front door. Everything was as I remembered it, even the dining room. I put my backpack down, and put my hand out to Mai Ling. She took it, and said, "Come and sit. We will talk over some tea, and you must meet my son."

Mai Ling was widowed and had a son, whose name was Lee, after his father, who had died three years earlier. Lee was now twenty-six: five foot four, stockily built, black hair cut very short, and he had a smiley face like his mother. His English was excellent. He told me about his workshop, and his employees making jewellery and fake Rolex watches! I was invited to visit, so after many cups of tea and much chat, Lee took me to his workshop in his Mercedes car. I saw much delicate work with gold and stones – starting with smelting gold recovered from scrap.

When we returned to the house, Mai Ling had a meal ready for us, and it was wonderful. I felt as if I was living in the past and would see old friends walk through the door any minute. The house was strangely quiet. I asked Mai Ling about the old business.

"All change now. For many years we have just run the house as a guest house for tourists and business people. You must come and stay as our guest for as long as you wish." I thanked her.

"Do you remember the first job I did for your father at Flagstaff House? I have often thought of it, and what good it did, if any!"

"Jake, I can tell you now – it was to get you to work for us, nothing happened that night!"

"You mean I got money and a bank account for doing nothing?"

"No, not for nothing, you did come to work for us." I burst out laughing as I thought of the time I had worried about that night and any possible consequences.

We drank more tea and talked of the past. Afterwards Lee took me to the hotel to collect my rucksack, and then back to the house. I made myself comfortable in a high backed chair in the dining room, and drifted off into a world of my own. I began thinking about the gold bars Sunshine and I had found all those years ago. Would they still be there, or had someone found them? I'd never given it a thought over the years, and never spoken of it to anyone, as they would have said it was just bullshit – but I knew different – and, strange as it sounds, things like this do happen!

After I left the army I'd gone into business in the waste industry and made a successful business, selling it to one of the major operators twenty years later.

Mai Ling caught my eye as I looked up. I hadn't realised how long I'd been thinking to myself. "You're very quiet, Jake. Is something wrong?"

"No, Mai Ling, just memories. Do you remember the story we told you about the gold we found in Borneo back in 1963?"

"Yes, Jake, I do. Is that why you are here?"

"No, I've been through a bad time – marriage, divorce, bankruptcy – that's why I came out here for a rest, and to stay for a few months."

"Jake, you stay as long as you wish."

"Only after you bring me up to date on your life since we last met, Mai Ling." So I was brought up to date. Father had died. Mai Ling had married, Lee was born, then his father died and so on – the years passed and here we were.

Lee was looking on, and asked, "What happened all those years ago?" We made ourselves comfortable. Lee poured drinks, and his mother told the story. I watched as Lee listened. I could see the excitement as he waited for the next bit. When Mai Ling had finished, I asked Lee if he had ever been to Borneo.

"No, never, I did my jungle training in Singapore military for two years. Do you think you could find the gold, Jake?"

"Well, Lee, I'm convinced I can find the spot on the river we marked – but it would be a search from that point on, with the bearing that I've remembered as well as my army number. There'll be dangers, including piracy, bandits, and every crook in the Orient – maybe even Japs!"

"Do you think there are still Japs around after all this time, Jake?"

"I read about it not so long ago, and made a note about it." I rummaged in my rucksack for some press cuttings and read out the newsprint.

"'Lubang Islands in the Philippines Group, 1974: a Japanese soldier, Hiroo Onada, who had been hiding in the mountains of Lubang for thirty years, finally decided to give himself up as a WW2 prisoner of war. A further discovery in April 1980 on Mount Halcon on the island of Mindoro, not far from Lubang Island: Captain Fumio Nakahira, Imperial Japanese Army, aged 74, gave himself up as a WW2 POW.' So you see, it's possible some still remain, mostly on islands – as headhunters would find them on the mainland. I saw many Jap heads in the longhouses of Borneo. "

Mai Ling didn't look too happy about the way the conversation was going, but added, "Lee, you're a man now and can make up you own mind, but you would be in good hands. I could trust no one more than my old friend, Jake, and he is the only one left alive who has seen this gold. "

So we started planning right away, soon realising this was going to be a costly exercise. Security was utmost in my mind. Firstly, we couldn't involve anyone else until we knew the gold was there. We had to find it.

Two weeks went by before we departed Singapore for Kota Kinabalu, as Jesselton was now known. We arrived, dressed as backpackers, and took a bus out to Likas. Having checked into Feredas Bed and Breakfast for three days, we then took a flight to Tawau (a frontier town near the Indonesian border). The Marco Polo Hotel was the best in town, with its own generator, as the town lights went out every hour – a result of overload.

The town was five times the size I remembered it. We observed people being rounded up at gunpoint and loaded onto trucks. I asked a shopkeeper, "What's happening?"

"They are illegal immigrants," I was told. "Ship them out today. They come back again tonight!"

We went off to find Borneo divers, to see about the hire of jet skis and boats. A very nice young lady directed us to agents used by them. We hired a good sized boat, with a crew of two, ready to leave next morning as soon as we got the jet skis delivered and loaded.

The next morning after a good breakfast, we departed Tawau pier with more locals looking on than I would have liked, but then they weren't used to seeing tourists. We headed westward for the entrance to the river Serudong. Soon the jungle was closing in around us, and the air was becoming humid and sticky, with that smell of decaying vegetation. It wasn't long till we were passing Kalabakan to our right. It was just a cluster of bamboo huts and a few wooden bungalows. The only signs of life were one old man fishing and a boy playing with his dog. I could see smoke from cooking fires, but not much else, so we went past as if unnoticed. I knew the place we had to find was fifteen, maybe twenty miles further up river. An hour passed, and I ordered a stop. The skipper edged the craft into the bank, and the crew made secure.

Lee and I lowered the jet skis over the side and started off up river, to the amusement of the crew. Well, this was the way to travel! Although noisy, it was fast. I was watching for beach areas to my right. These would have changed over the years with the monsoon rains, so we'd have to check out most of them. Lee was enjoying himself, and found it was fun to stand on the seat of his jet ski, till he suddenly fell off and I nearly went over him! That put an end to the fun. We checked out beach after beach, and then we found a place that looked right and went ashore.

"Lee, this looks like it. God, this is uncanny!" A chill went through me. There, right in front of me, was the tree with the signal wire tied round it – as if it was only yesterday that Sunshine and I put it there. I started to move stones at the base of the tree, and it wasn't long before I found the rubbish, or what remained of it – foil-wrapped jam and cheese tubes. I looked round at Lee. He was handing me the remains of 7.62 mm cases, which must have been here since the time we had fired at the canoes, or it could have been later, for all we knew.

We started a fire, made a brew, and ate some cold rice and fish. There was nothing else we could do today, but return down river to the boat for the night. It only took twenty minutes to get back to the boat: what with an outgoing tide we went about twice as fast as on calm waters. We told the skipper we'd found a good place to camp tomorrow, and we would be able to explore further up river from there and see if there were any longhouses. He could return to Tawau and come back in two days' time to pick us up here. We settled in for the night – a good night's sleep – as we were going to be up with the dawn, and on our way with our rucksacks and extra fuel on a small tow raft.

We soon found our way back to the beach and pulled the jet skis from the water, securing them in a fold in the ground. Lee tied them to a tree, in case of a sudden flood, and covered them with foliage: one, we didn't want any visitors and two, we didn't fancy the jets getting washed away and leaving us stranded here!

"Right, Lee, we're going in on a bearing of 45 degrees for one hour, and then we make camp. As far as I remember, it wasn't hard going – mostly large forest timber, the ground flat with a few bumps here and there. You go first, and I'll check the bearing from behind."

We lifted our rucksacks and were soon swallowed up by the forest. I'd forgotten just how small we were among these giant trees – we were like ants in tall grass. "Go left a little, Lee. I'm marking our trail so we can find our way back." I made split bamboo markers, each twenty inches long, which I would stick in the ground within sight of each other, as I didn't want to leave a permanent trail – such as cut or broken branches, looking like a motorway for everyone to follow. After an hour, we stopped and made camp. There was nothing I could recognise. We slung our hammocks and our rain covers over the top, and got some food on the go, whilst we discussed plans for the next day. I showed Lee how we would have to search from this point like a fan, on bearings twelve degrees apart for five hundred yards each, working our way around the compass.

"This could take a long time, Jake."

"I know, but there's no other way. We travel light, water and machetes." Lee was handing me a mess tin of curry and rice. We sat eating and chatting. Then I said, "We still have a few hours of light yet. Shall we try a bearing, Jake?"

"OK, let's do it."

I could tell the excitement in both of us. "Let's continue on the line of march for five hundred yards." Lee led off, but after just two hundred yards the ground fell away, down a steep bank to running water. "I never crossed water the last time I was here. Let's go back, Lee, and try another bearing."

The next bearing was twelve degree to the right of our line of march. After five hundred yards, more water was flowing from our right, so we returned to the campsite for the night. We climbed into our hammocks and slept for a few hours, until I woke to the sound of rain bucketing down, and the fire hissing as it was extinguished. I lay for hours listening to the rain, and then it stopped as quickly as it had started. The water dripped off the leaves for the next hour or two, and then came the first sign of the dawn. The jungle came alive with the dawn chorus of birds, monkeys and insects. I climbed out of my hammock, very stiff and damp. The vegetation underfoot was very wet, but not muddy. Lee was up and about, and had the kettle on the Hex burner for a brew, and I was feeling my age now. Although I was in some pain, I wouldn't give in to it – I still craved the adventure. Even if this was a fruitless exercise, I was still enjoying myself.

The jungle was warming up, and starting to steam as we set off on the next bearing. We did four out to five hundred yards, and drew a blank. I sat down and pulled out my water bottle, wiped my face and drank some water. I could hear Lee exploring around, not far from me, on the left, and then he was back.

"Jake, come!" He turned, and I was on my feet and following him. There, just in front of us, was the engine.

"We've found it! After all that marching about! If you hadn't gone on a little further, Lee, we would have been back at the campsite trying another bearing and maybe never have found it."

"Jake, you stay here and rest and I will go back and fetch the camping gear." He was off again, but I couldn't rest now. I got my machete out and started to cut away creepers and vine, and worked my way round the engine. We would never have seen it if Lee hadn't practically walked into it. The boxcar, or what was left of it, was just a rusting metal frame – the termites having eaten the rest – the same with the sleepers. I worked my way round to the spot where Sunshine and I had slept. From there, I got my bearings to the entrance to the bunker, only a few yards away. Lee was back with most of our gear, having left spare rations, water and non-essentials back at the campsite, sealed in plastic bin liners.

It didn't take long for the two of us to uncover the entrance and drop down into the hole. The wooden boxes had gone! My heart sank at the thought of someone else having arrived there first, then I saw old metal fittings – all that remained of the boxes – and I realised the termites had taken the rest.

The entrance to the main chamber was half full of soil, there being just enough room to crawl inside. I went first, and prayed there were no snakes as I flashed my torch about from side to side. Lee was right behind me. We stood there, shining our torches about. The interior had changed: there was soil in piles, roots down to the floor, the wooden boxes had gone and guns lay everywhere, again just rusty metal. Then I saw something shining further back. Lee had the two gas lanterns going now. We went further in and stopped.

"Jake, I wasn't expecting a sight like this – this is truly amazing!"

"I never expected it either, Lee. Sunshine and I only opened two boxes; there must be a few hundred bars here. This place is very different now to the way it was. Remember, it was only sixteen years after the Second World War the last time I was here, now all the boxes have rotted away. What a mess! We'd better get organised. We'd best start by opening up the entrance and bringing our gear in here."

We cleared the entrance and started to move the gold bars and stack them just inside. Some of them were buried in soil, but it didn't take much to uncover them. We now had a total of four hundred and seventy-two bars.

Several hours went by before we took a break, and started looking around to see what else we could find. I turned my attention to what looked like another entrance that had caved in. I'd noticed it the last time I was here, but didn't venture near it with Sunshine. Now, as I drew near, I could see over the pile of soil that it was another room.

"Lee, bring one of the lamps over here!" I was at work with my trenching tool, and had cleared the top of the mound by the time Lee arrived with the lamp.

"You hold the lamp, Jake. I go first this time." Lee crawled over the top and I followed. We were standing in a room, eight feet by ten, with another door – intact this time – at the far end. There was a radio transmitter lying smashed and rusty on the floor, with the remains of a bamboo table and chairs, two oil lamps, and some broken plates and bowls. I picked up a bamboo container about twelve inches long, and pulled it apart to reveal a roll of papers. I closed it, and put it in my pack for examination later. On the wall there was a faded Jap flag and the words 'Kempei Tai'. Beside it were three names scrawled in English and a small Australian flag.

I started prising the rusty steel door open, until it came away with little effort. Lee shone his torch into the darkness. There was a small gauge railway with two bogie cars. "Well, what have we found now?" said Lee.

"Let's check it out."

"Stop, Lee!" I shouted. He froze.

"Look just in front of your left foot."

"I see it." It was a steel plate pressure trap fitting between the rails. On close examination, we could see the trip hammer spring-loaded, and in good order. We could see it clearly from our direction, but it would be impossible to see if we had come in from the other direction.

"That will come up and hit this thing on the wall – what is it, Jake?" I shone my torch on the object that was sticking through the iron cladding of the tunnel wall, and could see into the hole.

"Holy shit, it's a bomb – an aircraft bomb by the looks of it." I put out my hand and touched it. It was greasy and looked like new. "The crafty bastards!"

"Jake, it looks like it was intended for strangers coming from the other direction; you wouldn't see any of it."

"We'd best look for more. Let's make safe this trigger."

"You hold down the hammer and I'll unhook the spring."

"Strange, there were none in the main chamber, Lee! Thank the sweet Jesus for that! I never considered traps!"

"When you fell into this place the first time, I think it was not open to the outside. You fell into an area that was a tunnel just about to be completed when the Japs left in a big hurry. This is the true entrance, some distance ahead of us."

We dismantled the trigger and continued along the tunnel. We reached two hundred yards and came to a passing place. The tunnel had been constructed of corrugated steel like an air-raid shelter. It was in very good condition, with just a few holes here and there. The floor was earth and small stones from the river, with puddles every few yards. We continued on for nearly an hour, moving very slowly, till we came to a pile of earth and green shrubbery.

"Looks like the way out, Jake." Lee was hacking at the under-growth, and soon managed to get out of the tunnel. As our eyes got used to the light we saw we were still in the forest, but we could hear the river close by – we were within fifty yards of it. We stood on the river bank, looking in both directions, and trying to figure out if our beach was left or right. We both came to the same conclusion – we didn't recognise this part of the river, so we marked the spot and turned down river. As we rounded the first bend, we saw the beach and the hide for the jet skis. We didn't fancy going back through the tunnel, so we went back to the site of the first night's camp, collected the rest of our kit, and made our way back to the train.

"We'll have to sleep beside the train tonight in case there's rain and a cave-in. The roof down there is not too clever."

"I think there are ghosts down there, Jake!"

"You're right, Lee – better up here."

The next morning we changed our plan for the day. We decided to move the gold across the bunker to the railway bogies, and use that tunnel to bring the gold near to the river. This was going to save us many trips to the river on foot, with just a few bars at a time. We greased the bogie wheels, with grease from the bomb and a few tubes of army cheese, to make them run smoother. It took us all morning to move the bars and load the two bogies, and there was still more for a second and third trip. Lee started pushing the first and I watched as it gathered speed. I followed, and it wasn't long before we reached the far end. I was very surprised the bogies stayed on the lines, as they didn't look too straight. We unloaded, and pushed the bogies back for the second load, then did the same again for the third run to get the remaining bars and our kit.

At the final exit point, we placed two bars each into the bottom of our rucksacks and covered them with other items. Other bits of equipment, we put in bin liners and left.

We made our way to the jet skis and were soon underway back down river to the meeting point for the boat. We arrived there before the boat, had a swim in the river then made ourselves comfortable, eating rice and fish, having a brew and a well-earned rest.

Late in the afternoon we heard the sound of the engine. Soon the boat appeared around the bend and edged into the bank. The crew were all smiles and chatting away, most likely about mad tourists. They spoke no English. I knew Lee spoke Malay, and that was enough to get by, but I wouldn't trust this lot further than I could throw them – if they'd known what we had in our rucksacks, we would have had our throats cut at the first opportunity. After loading the jets onboard, we asked the skipper to depart now before it got dark. I wanted to get out of the river and back to Tawau before dark. The crew weren't too keen, but I knew that when we got to sea, visibility would be better than in the river, and safer for us.

We emerged from the river as it was getting dark, but we had a clear view out across the sea and would soon be back in Tawau. We tied up at the jetty at about 2000 hours and settled down on deck for the night, using our rucksacks as pillows. Lee and I took turns to sleep till dawn. We said our goodbyes to the crew, and made our way into town to catch a bus for the nine-hour journey to Kota Kinabalu, over winding mountain roads through thick jungle. We couldn't risk flying, as there was a chance our kit would be searched. So, after one hell of a journey, we arrived very tired, stiff and hungry. We made our way to Feredas Bed and Breakfast for a good night's rest.

Our next stop was the ferry to the island of Labuan to see a bank manager, who was known to Lee when he had worked in the bank in Singapore. The bank was a modern building with plenty of dark glass and armed security guards at the door. We were asked to leave our rucksacks outside. No chance! Lee asked security to make contact with the manager. Soon a clerk showed up at the front door and took details, and then went back inside. Twenty minutes went by before he returned and asked us to follow him. We were shown into a very plush office.

"Ah, Lee, It is good to see you after so long. Sorry about so much security. Put your packs down and have a seat."

"Mr Yew, this is my friend, Jake."

I took his hand. It was limp like a pound of cold cod. "Pleased to meet you, Mr Yew," I lied.

I didn't like the look of the man. His eyes were black, and darting about like a shit-house rat; his face was pockmarked; his teeth were yellow, and his arms looked short on his fat little body. Already he was smelling money. He sank into his high-backed chair, looked from one to the other and pressed a bell on his desk. The door opened and a girl entered.

"Gentlemen, will you take some refreshment? Tea, coffee, Coke?"

"Cokes will be fine, Mr Yew," said Lee, nodding to me.

"Well, my friends, what can I do for you?"

"We need money, lots of it," I said. The door opened. It was the girl with the refreshments. She placed the tray on the table, and left. "Mr Yew, we need money for a business venture, about four hundred thousand US dollars."

He looked at us and burst out laughing. We looked at ourselves and laughed too – we didn't look the business part, in our dirty shirts and denims.

"You have collateral, I suppose?" More laughter.

I reached into my pack for one of the bars, wrapped in rag. I placed it on his desk and unwrapped it. He sat for a full minute staring at the bar – not laughing now – his hand was shaking as he lifted it. "Do you have more?"

"Yes, we have located more. That's why we need money," I said.

"This bar is about twelve kilos and this number, 893, I don't know what that means, but I can find out for you."

"We have four with us to deposit. They all have the same number," said Lee.

"How many are there, Lee?"

"We don't know yet," I butted in. "They're on the sea bed," I lied again.

"There is more than enough security for the money you need, and more anytime. I will put this in my safe. Are you both staying in Victoria tonight, gentlemen? If so, you must join me for dinner." We accepted his invitation, looking at ourselves again.

"Best get cleaned up, with some new clothes. Think we can get an advance?" We laughed as we went downstairs to the tellers and got some funds.

We dined well that night with Mr Yew. He was on his own, but the subject of gold repeatedly came up and we kept changing the subject. Then two beautiful girls were introduced by Mr Yew. "Gentlemen, I thought you could do with some company tonight, so I arranged these ladies for you."

Waiters rushed over to pull out chairs, and the two sat down. I had the feeling we were being set up. I looked at Lee, and could see he was thinking the same.

"That was very nice of you, Mr Yew, but you should not have gone to so much trouble," I said.

"No trouble at all, Jake."

We chatted away to the girls. I don't even remember their names. All I wanted was for Mr Yew to say goodnight and bugger off. It turned out he did, but left on the note that the girls were ours until tomorrow morning. Now we were stuck with them – a refusal would mean we had something to hide. We all went upstairs to our rooms where, as I thought, the questions started but got them nowhere. We managed to rid ourselves of the two girls before we went in to breakfast. Someone wasn't going to be happy when they reported in with no information!

"Jake, we'd best watch our backs. I didn't like the line of questions – those girls knew too much!"

"Do you trust Mr Yew?"

"Who trusts any bank manager?"

"This one smells gold, but we need him for now. Lee, I still have this bamboo container in my pack – how about we take a look at the contents before I forget about it again."

I handed Lee the container, and he pulled it apart and removed the papers. Lee very carefully unrolled the papers and placed them on the table. They were all in Japanese and there were two maps – one of the tunnel, and the other of the rail line, shown as a dotted line going to an area that looked like a camp, about one thousand yards north of the tunnel entrance.

"I don't think they got that far. The war must have finished before they expected." I said. "I will send the papers to Singapore for Mai Ling to check out. OK, Lee?"

Chapter 10

The *Dragon* Boat

So we arrived in the Philippines, with plenty of US dollars to spend. We looked around the docks in Manila, but decided the place was too busy. We were attracting too much attention so we headed north, by road, to the old US Naval base at Subic Bay. There were just a few US navy personnel remaining at the base for handover to the Philippines government. It was not long before we found a local doing business with the navy, and telling us he could get us anything we wanted. Well, we found a thirty-six foot fishing vessel with twin diesels, in good condition, as it had been the property of a navel officer who had now returned to his home in America, having sold it to a young US sailor called Larry. That evening we met Larry at a local bar and did a deal for the boat, and paid him cash. After a few beers we discovered Larry was one of three men in the stores on base, disposing of US surplus stocks. We said we would be interested in seeing what was on offer, and were then invited to meet with Larry next morning on the base.

After breakfast we rushed off to the base and found Larry waiting at the main gate to book us in. Security was still run by US MPs. The three of us headed for the vast storage building – an aircraft hangar, which was stacked with twenty-foot high racks, stretching the length of the building. There were lines of jeeps, trucks, field guns, mortars, and racks of firearms. We walked around inspecting everything: this was amazing, just what we needed; we could not believe our luck! We purchased: four CAR; fifteen 5.56 mm assault rifles; four colt 45s automatic pistols; two M60 7.62 mm machine guns and a mounting rack; several boxes of ammunition, fragmentation and smoke grenades; one M79 grenade launcher, flares; two dozen claymore mines; hand held radios; a first aid box (big enough for a field hospital); and a

Vietnamese crossbow. We purchased all items as government surplus and paid cash. Larry obtained permission for us to bring our boat alongside the store building jetty, and arranged for all items to be boxed and loaded.

"You guys going to start a war?" Larry asked.

"No, just a little security for our journey through these pirate infested waters," I replied.

"Can't be too careful in this part of the world friend," said Larry.

We departed the jetty waving our farewell to Larry and his two friends, and headed out to sea. The boat responded well and the engines gave us a good fifteen knots. Our next destination was Puerto Galera on the island of Mindoro – a full day's cruising lay ahead. It was growing dark as we were passing the island of Lubang, and it became obvious to us we were not going to make Mindoro tonight, so we headed into a small fishing port on Lubang island. We anchored about five hundred yards out, our strong arc lamps lighting the area around us for a good one hundred yards. The diesel engine driving the generator was pounding away at a steady fifteen hundred revs a minute, keeping the lights and radar going, and there was no chance of anyone coming near us without us noticing.

Lee came up to the wheelhouse with the evening meal, after which we checked the weapons, placing two assault rifles along with pistols in the wheelhouse, for easy reach. We took turns to keep watch till dawn, then we raised the anchor and set sail south for Porto Galera, just a few hours away.

We found a quiet corner of the dock to carry out our work on the boat. Lee went off to phone his mother, and arrange for two of his old army pals to join us in two days' time. He and I worked away making the boat look more like a fishing boat. We purchased fishing nets, rope and floats, laying them on deck, along with oil drums and other fishing essentials. We overhauled the engine parts and the air compressor. We greased the steering cables and rudder mountings. The twin M60 machine guns were in the wheelhouse ready to be mounted on pre-arranged mounts: one on the bridge, one port, one starboard and one aft. We rigged up a flame thrower using a half inch steel pipe, six feet long, mounted on a tripod with a swivel clamp. One end of the pipe was connected to a mixer valve and the compressor, the other to a rubber hose running from a drum of diesel fuel. We used a gas hose attached to a gas bottle with a simple burner to ignite the pressurised diesel air mix. Now all we had to do was test it, but not here.

Lee named the boat and painted a fire breathing Dragon on the bow, in bright colours. A taxi arrived on the dock, and Lee ran up the gang plank to greet his friends from Singapore.

"Jake, this is Kee Lim – very good cook; and this ugly one is Fuk Yew – son of Tang."

"Pleased to meet you both, I remember your father; Tang was a good man and loyal servant to Lee's family. Come on board and stow your gear, then Lee will show you round the boat."

We departed Porto Galera with the dawn coming up fast and a calm sea, then headed south-east down the coast of Mindoro, turning south-west and heading out into the Sulu Sea. We saw plenty of sea traffic: fishing boats, cargo ships, tankers, and ferries but no one paid any attention to us. By nightfall we reached the Cagayan Islands and pulled into a bay surrounded by dense jungle, hanging from steep slopes and looking impassable. There was no beach, the only way of approach to our position was from the sea, and the opening was about two hundred yards across. Lee and Kee took the inflatable boat, with its thirty-five horse power engine, and did a tour of the island, returning twenty minutes later to say the island was deserted and looked the same all round.

We set up the flame thrower on the aft deck so we could swing it ninety degrees left and right – now was the time to try it out. Lee lit the gas burner and Kee opened the tap from the compressor with a hiss. I then opened the valve on the fuel drum, and immediately the air fuel mixture ignited with a flash. The flame shot out about seventy yards lighting up the whole bay and bringing the jungle creatures screaming out of their slumber: monkeys, bats and wild birds – the noise was overpowering as we shut off the fuel and air and returned to the darkness. Things went quiet just a quickly as they had come alive. We covered the flame thrower with a tarpaulin and turned on the floodlamps to give us visibility in case of approach from the sea.

We settled in for the night after laughing ourselves silly. The evening meal was prepared by Kee. Lee and I took the first watch, handing over to the other two at midnight. Dawn came without incident and we left the bay and set our course south for the port of Zamboanga, on the western tip of Mindanao. I opened up the twin diesel engines to 2,500 revolutions per minute, and our speed increased giving us a cooling breeze.

It was late afternoon when we sited Zamboanga. The port was very busy as we approached, a berth being indicated to us by the harbourmaster. After tying up, the harbourmaster came aboard to ask our business. Lee told him we were on our way to a dive centre on the island of Tawi-Tawi. That seemed to satisfy him as he looked around the deck, then he climbed back up the ladder to the jetty and we sighed with relief.

It was time to fuel, and stock up the galley for the long haul to Borneo; three hundred miles south-west, passing to the north of Basilan and Jolo Island, and on to Tawi-Tawi. We had to spend the night tied up under the full view of every curious local, looking at this strange vessel. There was no sleep for any of us that night.

We were pleased to depart Zamboanga at first light. It was only then we could catch up on sleep, two at a time. Night came and we slowed down and kept a close watch on the radar scanner, as there were many small islands and reefs in this area, and plenty of small fishing boats with their lights on going about their business. We sailed through the night and arrived at the island of Tawi-Tawi just after first light, anchoring one hundred yards out from the white sandy beach, lined with coconut palms. The water was as clear as crystal. After a good breakfast Fuk and Kee went over the side for a swim, while Lee and I watched from the deck armed with our assault rifles just in case sharks showed up. Then it was our turn to enjoy the cooling water. Back on deck, we filled one bucket with fresh water to use to wash the salt water off our bodies – we could not spare any more as water was limited till we found our next filling point. Lee and Kee went ashore and later returned with mangos and coconuts. Just after their return, local islanders found us and stood on the beach looking us over. It was time for us to move on again before too many locals turned up. We slowly moved out to sea and continued south-westerly, still in Philippine controlled waters. Lee was in the wheelhouse, tuned into the radio, and watching the radar when he shouted for me to come to the wheelhouse. He had picked up news that five western tourists had been kidnapped by pirates from a dive centre on the island of Sipadan in Borneo waters, about eighty miles ahead on our present bearing. We called Kee and Fuk to the wheelhouse and told them the news.

"Best we stay very alert now! Fuk, take my binoculars up above the wheelhouse and spot any vessels ahead. Lee, stay on the wheel and watch the radar – we don't know if the pirates will be heading in our direction or west to Indonesian water."

"Jake, I would think that from the position of Sipadan they would head east into Philippine waters, just a short journey, and out of reach from the Malaysian police sea patrols."

"I have to admit I think you're right, Lee."

"I go make food now," said Kee, hurrying off to the galley.

It was mid-afternoon when Lee spotted a vessel ahead of us on the radar heading in our direction, but Fuk did not have a visual on it yet, there being a number of small islands and coral reefs ahead on the horizon. Then came an excited cry from up above – it was Fuk shouting, "I see boat ahead!"

"OK, we sail past them about two hundred yards clear and look them over. I need to know how many are on board, any white faces, weapons! I will stay in the wheelhouse – I don't want them alerted by the sight of a white man – wave to them as we pass and keep your guns out of sight."

As we drew level with them, I could see them clearly now – two figures on the bow watching us. I moved the wheel to the right just a touch to give us good clearance. I didn't fancy getting too close to this vessel – it was a large sampan, but motorised and making good speed. As we came broadside

Lee, Kee and Fuk waved, and the waves were returned. The vessel disappeared to our rear in a cloud of diesel fumes.

"Anyone see anything?"

"Yes, Jake, I count eight men and they don't have radar or radio," said Kee.

"I see white people sitting under canopy at rear. You would not see them from the deck, but from above the wheelhouse with the binoculars I get good view," said Fuk.

"Lee, get back on the radar and don't lose them. Keep radio silence."

"Should we not radio for help, Jake?" asked Fuk.

"No point: Malaysian patrols won't come into these waters; and Philippine patrols are not an option, even if we could contact them – too far away. We are the only chance those people have."

I brought our vessel about and asked Lee to keep us out of visual sight of that sampan. We cruised for over an hour back the way we came, weaving between the small islands and reefs.

Then Lee shouted. "They have stopped, nine miles ahead between two small islands!"

"All ahead one third, bring us to six miles, they won't see us."

We watched the target on the radar, came to six miles, and could now see the two islands but not their vessel. We dropped anchor and waited for the approaching night. It was dark and cloudy as we raised the anchor and closed in, with just one engine ticking over and no night lights. We positioned ourselves two miles from the first island, which was screening us from their position on the other side. We dropped anchor and sat and looked through the binoculars at the shoreline – no sign of life, good!

Lee and I took the inflatable and paddled the two miles to the beach, and hid the inflatable in the rocks on the shoreline. We looked back and could not see the *Dragon* in the dark. I led the way with my assault rifle at the ready, Lee covering my rear. We headed in an anti-clockwise direction round the island, and it was not long before we saw the sampan. As we got nearer we saw a fire burning on the beach opposite us, with four men around it chattering away. We could hear them, but not pick up any of the chat. Lee spotted three others on the sampan – that left one possible below deck.

"OK, Lee. Let's get back."

We returned to the inflatable and started to row back into the dark, and were within three hundred yards before we saw a yellow glow stick and saw the *Dragon*. "What we do now Jake?" asked Kee.

"We plan our attack." There were grins all round.

"We don't want the tourists hurt so it will have to be silent and quick," I said.

"We know there are four on board and four ashore, that could change any time, and we don't have any silenced weapons," said Lee.

"Yes, we do! We have the crossbow," said Fuk. We burst out laughing as we thought about it. I got to thinking that a crossbow and my two knives could just be possible.

"Kee, you stay onboard and watch for my signal from the shore.

I will flash my torch – three rapid pauses then another three – you bring the *Dragon* inshore with lights on."

Lee, Fuk and I got into the inflatable along with rifles and the crossbow, a box of grenades and two claymore mines, and headed for the island. We landed at the same spot we had on the first trip. Lee and Fuk walked round the island till they saw the fire opposite and the sampan between, but now there were six men sitting around the fire eating and chatting; that left two onboard. Lee and Fuk hurried back to my position with the inflatable.

"Right my friends, we attack from the sea. We close in on the sampan, keeping it between us and the fire on the beach."

We paddled round the island and out beyond the sampan, staying in the dark. The sampan was lit by oil lamps and, as we closed in on the port side, I could see one man near the bow looking towards the shore but could not see the other.

"Fuk, take out the man on the deck with the crossbow when you are ready. Lee and I will paddle closer."

We were now just fifteen feet away when Fuk loosed off his first bolt – it passed right through the man and he dropped dead without a sound. We paddled to the side of the vessel and I jumped onto the deck, crouching down. Lee was right behind me with his assault rifle. I signalled him not to fire; I could hear western voices to the rear but no sign of the other pirate. Fuk was now on board and checking the body of his kill. I was just about to move forward when a hatch slid open to my left, and a figure emerged calling for his mate. I moved fast, grabbing his hair and knifing him through the windpipe – he went limp and dropped back through the hatch. A quick look through the hatch revealed our tourists sitting, roped together, and looking very frightened.

I dropped through the hatch and a voice said, "Who are you?"

"Don't be scared, make no noise, I'm British."

"Are we glad to see you mate!"

"No talking, follow my instructions."

There were four men and one woman – they looked terrified. I cut each of them loose, and whispered to them that my men were on deck, and to follow their directions. They moved up onto the deck, I had a quick look around. Lee passed three grenades down to me, and I pulled the pin out of the first one and placed it under the body lying at my feet. I placed the second under a box, then climbed up on deck and placed the third under the body on the foredeck. I looked towards the shore and could see the pirates around the fire chatting and laughing, and completely unaware of what had just taken place. They were in for a surprise when they returned to their sampan and moved their dead pals.

I joined the others on the inflatable, now well overcrowded, so we sat legs astride the floatation tanks. Fuk was sitting legs astride the bow, while Lee and I paddled out to sea and rounded the island. Once we were safe I flashed my torch and then saw the navigation lights of *Dragon* come on and the sound of the engine. As it came alongside we all scrambled on board.

"Kee, get us out of here south-west!"

The *Dragon* came about and the engines roared as we put distance between us and the island. Then a voice said, "Who the hell are you guys?"

"I'm British, and my friends here are from Singapore. We were on our way to Borneo from the Philippines when we heard the news and kept a watch. We spotted you earlier today and turned to follow."

"Ah! That was you we saw when we were sitting under the sun canopy. We thought you had not seen us. They moved us inside when we got to the island. We were giving up hope mate. My name is John, I'm from Aus and so is Fred there. Hans and his wife, Astrid, are Dutch, and Paul is French."

"Well you can all relax now. Like a beer?" I handed the beer around. "Really like something to eat. We have had no food or a wash since we were taken," said Astrid.

"You will eat well tonight; try some mango while we get a meal going."

"We can let you have two buckets of water and soap; we are short on fresh water."

I brought the water, soap and two towels. Kee provided a pair of combat trousers, a blue denim shirt, flip-flops and a comb for Astrid. Astrid went behind a screen, hastily erected by Fuk; the four guys shared the second bucket and finished before Astrid. When she returned she looked a different person in clean fatigues; her blonde shoulder length hair combed out, drying in the warm night air.

Lee was back in the wheelhouse, Kee and Fuk were in the galley, and our visitors still had many questions to ask.

The meal arrived and we sat on deck with our new friends, as they ate well without a sound. I handed round more beer and they all started chatting and giving thanks for their rescue. I thanked Lee, Kee and Fuk for a successful outcome to the day's events.

"Lucky you fellows were armed," said John.

"Not wise to travel in these waters without insurance," Lee said.

"We are going to take you back to Sipadan – it's our next stop, and I think the tourist operators and police will be delighted to get you back."

"Can you radio ahead and let them know we are on the way?" asked Astrid.

"It is best for us to keep radio silence – don't want any more trouble and we don't know who is tuned in. We will be there by dawn, and please don't mention firearms – just crossbow and knives – as we are not supposed to be armed, and we will be entering Malaysian waters in one hour! When we land I will have to give a report to the police," I said. Everyone nodded in agreement.

Sipadan came into sight at first light. It was a small island used as a dive centre, consisting of a few huts on the beach, and a two-man police post. We headed for the wooden jetty; there was a police patrol boat alongside, armed with twin machine guns front and rear, three policemen on deck watching us as we came alongside. Suddenly the police became excited as the hostages stepped ashore; then a little fat man, in a Borneo Divers' T-shirt and denim shorts, recognised the Westerners and started shouting. Soon the jetty area was a hive of activity as friends were reunited. We were made welcome by Borneo Divers and asked to stay the night. We accepted the hospitality and I made my report to the police, who in turn interviewed all concerned. Late in the afternoon a second police vessel arrived with the chief of police who clearly wanted a first hand report. Later I was sent for and thanked on a very successful rescue, and told that if there was anything we needed, to ask or contact himself at police HQ in Tawau. He later joined us for the evening meal laid on by the dive centre, and a very enjoyable night was had by all.

The next morning after breakfast we said farewell to our new friends and swapped phone numbers and addresses. They all came down to the jetty to wave us off, and it was all quite emotional. We headed out to sea and continued our course south-west for Tawau, arriving late afternoon and berthed alongside the jetty. The harbour-master came aboard and announced he knew all about us and our rescue, and that the story would be in the papers by tomorrow. I asked if we could fuel up before dark as we wished to be underway at first light. The harbourmaster arranged everything for us. I was somewhat concerned that we were now known in the area.

After fuelling up with diesel, fresh water and provisions, we moved out to a buoy in the harbour and tied up for the night. Lee and I went ashore in the inflatable to phone Mai Ling, and bring her up to date on our adventures. After the phone call we crossed the road and found a table at a hawker stall and ordered a beer. As I became aware of a man watching us from a stall behind Lee, I spoke quietly to Lee and warned him. I was surprised at his response when he said there was one behind me too. We ignored the two and finished our beer, stood up and made our way back to the jetty. Halfway there, Lee bent down to fix his bootlace and look behind – the two were following. We climbed down to the inflatable and returned to the *Dragon*. As we came alongside, Kee helped us aboard.

We sat on deck and told the other two what had happened. "Maybe the newspaper men have heard our story," said Kee.

"If that was the case why did they not approach us?" Lee said.

"Jake, you stay here. Fuk and I will go back ashore. Kee can take us in the inflatable to the far side of the jetty, out of site, and wait for us while we have a look around."

"OK, but no guns; one radio for emergency use only. I think Kee is better off back here, I don't want anyone on their own."

Kee pulled the inflatable round to the seaward side, Lee and Fuk climbed in and off went the three of them into the dark. Twenty minutes later I heard Kee paddling back; he tied up and came on board.

"Jake, Lee said to tell you that the two men are still on the jetty looking our way."

This was looking very sinister. I looked through the binoculars along the jetty, but could not make out much detail, with the town street lights behind. We waited and waited: two hours passed then we got a radio message.

"Back at pick up point." It was Lee.

"OK, Kee, go get them. Make sure they are alone before you land. Take this radio just in case of trouble."

Time dragged till Kee returned with the other two. Lee announced that our friend, Mr Yew, our friendly bank manager was at the Marco Polo Hotel.

"How did you find that out, Lee?"

"Saw the two men on the jetty head back into town and we followed. Saw them enter the hotel and go to reception. We were just about to leave when Mr Yew came into the picture. Just got lucky, I think!"

"Now why would he be here?" I said.

"The news of the rescue would have been on the radio, and it would not be hard for anyone to find us just now," said Fuk.

"I think he smells gold, Jake!"

"We still have the advantage that he is not aware that we know he is on to us; we go before dawn. Well Lee, you said never trust a bank manager!"

Chapter 11

The River of Death

Before first light we were under way, heading west for the mouth of the river Serudong, arriving on the rising tide to help us up the river. We soon passed Kalabakan, with early morning smoke rising gently on the still air from the cooking fires. Just one old man fishing and smoking his pipe watched us go by. The jungle was closing in on both sides as the river narrowed, the overhanging jungle making strange shadows. I felt the first trickle of sweat run down my back. Lee and Kee were up on the bow keeping a look out for the beach, but the tide was already turning and I was having difficulty making headway. We dropped anchor in midstream and it started to drag, so we dropped the second and came to a stop with a jerk as the anchors bit into roots on the river bed. We would now have to wait for the afternoon tide to continue our passage up river, about two miles.

All we could do now was eat and relax. Fuk and Lee set up fishing lines and let them drift astern, and it was not long before they were landing fish. I slept in the shade of the wheelhouse and was awakened by the smell of fish cooking. Kee had been busy, so it was fish and rice for a late lunch.

Lee had noticed that the river had slowed and was starting to rise; we watched the water rise to near the high wet mark on the bank. I started the engines and engaged forward to take the strain of the anchors; slowly they were brought on board, thick with mud.

We slowly proceeded and the river widened a little; it was not long till we saw the beach come into view. A little further round the next bend, near the tunnel entrance, we dropped both anchors in midstream and soon came to a stop. I closed down the engines and listened to the sound of the jungle and the river. Lee and Fuk were already getting a line ashore using the inflatable. I sat and watched the lads at work, and was thinking about that engine and how it came to be there. Kee noticed me and came over and sat down, so I shared my thoughts with him.

Kee said, "We used to go ashore on exercise from landing craft, and if the beach was soft the engineers would roll out sand mats for the vehicles. Maybe the Japs did the same."

"Got it! You could do the same with rails in a landing craft and a few extra rails and sleepers for the beach, and move forward by taking the rails from behind."

"That is very possible, Jake."

"Another thing is the engine and rails line up with the beach – that must have been the landing place."

"I go now and help the others with the loading, Jake."

Soon the inflatable was being pulled back and fore, between shore and the *Dragon* (now being loaded with gold bars!). Fuk and I had rigged lifting tackle, using the dinghy davits. This was handy to swing the loaded cargo net on board. While the inflatable was pulled ashore, Fuk and I passed the bars below deck, and packed ten bars into each box. It was a long job, and night had closed in before we had to finish and call it a day.

Next morning we started early, and by midday we had the load on board, and the *Dragon* was well down in the water – if there had been any more we would have been grounded.

"Lee, I would like a last look at the bunker before we go."

"OK, Jake, we go now."

I got my rucksack and rifle, and the two of us went ashore and headed back through the tunnel to the little room with the smashed radio set on the floor. In the main bunker we searched around. There was the forge, rusting rail fittings, the moulds for the gold casting, and the remains of the poor sods who had been made to work here, although mostly dust now! I would not have been surprised if there were not more victims nearby.

"Let's get out of here, Lee". We climbed out of the hole, close to the engine, and were glad to be back in the daylight again.

We headed for the river then Lee spoke. "Jake, we left the lantern on in the bunker!"

"I think we can afford a new one now!" We both started to laugh. Then came two rifle shots from the direction of the river; we went to ground and I found the radio in my pack, and made contact with Kee on the *Dragon*.

"It's OK, Jake. Fuk just shot a pig for tea," came the reply. By the time we got to the boat, the pig was hanging from the davit, cut open and cleaned.

"You scared the hell out of us back there," said Lee.

"You should have used the crossbow," I said.

"Should keep us fed for a week!" said Kee.

Fuk just grinned and carried on cutting up the pig. "Yes, Boss. I want to keep the skin – very useful!"

After the evening meal we sat on deck with just the oil lamps flickering, and the talk turned to what we would do with our share of the money. Kee was going to buy a rubber plantation, with a big house and car – and have lots of sons. Fuk was going home to Penang to buy all the brothels on the island, and offer package holidays to anyone who wanted one. Lee had no plans, but thought the armoury under his house would make a good hiding place for his money, with a few security arrangements added – and then he would expand his business empire.

"What are you going to do, Jake?" Lee asked.

"Me! I think I will buy a plantation in the Philippines with a big house – maybe get married and settle down."

"I can't see you settling down, Jake. You like adventure too much."

We turned in for the night as we intended to start the return journey at 0400 hours. Lee took the first watch and then handed over to Fuk. Half an hour later, Fuk was shaking me. "Wake up, Jake, come up on deck, quick!" I woke the other two as I passed them. I followed Fuk up to the wheelhouse.

"What is it Fuk?"

"I heard engine, now it has stopped."

The others joined us in the wheelhouse. We went out on the aft deck, and strained to see into the dark – there was no sound but the river.

"Get the guns mounted facing aft; uncover the flame thrower, slowly and no noise." My instincts were working overtime. I'd experienced this before, and when the jungle goes silent something is going to happen.

Lee handed me my binoculars – although not night vision, it was an improvement on eyesight. Now I could see two open boats with men paddling hard; no sign of a motor vessel – must be round the bend near the beach.

I counted six men in each boat. They would be able to see the *Dragon* easily with the oil lamps flickering, but not us lurking in the shadows on deck.

"OK, this looks like it's going to be a fire fight – wait for me to fire first. Ready the flame thrower."

Lee already had the gas burner lit. "Jake, the compressor tank is at full pressure," he whispered.

The boats were now close enough to see four men in each boat, and they were armed. Then the first grapple hook landed on the deck just missing Fuk. A second landed to my right, followed by a grenade hitting the hand rail and bouncing back into the river before exploding. "Fire!" I shouted.

All hell broke loose as the flame thrower spouted flame, lighting up the scene and catching one of the boats, turning the occupants to human torches – their screams were cut short as the twin M60s ripped through them. Lee swung the flame thrower onto the second boat, but the occupants were already in the river either dead or wounded. It was all over in seconds. Lee shut down the flame thrower. I shouted for Kee to get the engines running, put the arc lamps on and light up the area.

The jungle was alive with wildlife crashing through the bush and more bats than a horror film. As the lights came on we saw the full horror of what was floating around us on the rising river tide! One man was still struggling, but managed to grab a rope still attached to the *Dragon* by a grapple. "Kee, Fuk – get that man on board, I want answers." The guy was soon lying on the deck. He was burnt and had a stomach wound; he was not long for this world. "Well done lads. They were not expecting that reception!"

It was not long before we had the information we wanted, but the man died while being questioned. We put him back over the side to join his friends on their way down river.

"Jake, he said he is pirate working for a man, Ali Hamid, known as 'The Crow'. They were hired by a bank manager – he did not know his name. Their motor vessel is waiting downstream for them." I thanked Fuk.

"Lee, I want that bank manager. I will cut off his nuts when I get him!"

"Me too, Jake. Let's get after them before they can report this to Mr Yew."

I started the engine and took the strain. Kee and Fuk winched anchors on board. I started the turn, and the current did the rest. I kept slowly increasing the speed against the still incoming tide, hoping we would spot the pirate vessel round the next bend. Then as we came near to Kalabakan, we spotted a white cruiser with single mast and no radar; he was moving fast, churning up river mud, trying to make open water before we got too close.

I throttled back a little, keeping about one thousand yards, then I saw the change from muddy water to white water being churned up, and I knew we were entering open waters. "OK, here we go – guns ready!" I opened up the engines. We shot forward and started to gain on them. At five hundred yards Lee opened up with the twin machine guns, and rounds could be seen hitting their target and throwing up spouts of water around the vessel. Fire was being returned from their wheelhouse, but they did not seem to have our fire power.

We were now at two hundred yards, and Kee and Fuk opened up with anti-tank grenades fired from their rifles. Three landed in the water, the fourth hitting the stern of the vessel and destroying the engine compartment, bringing the vessel to a shuddering halt. The vessel burst into flames as we raced past pouring fire and grenades into her. She was going down stern first – we did not see any survivors as we sped past.

I had made up my mind to bypass Tawau as it was too close for comfort. The police could get word of a gun fight from fishing boats or locals we had not seen, and then there was the bank manger and his friends around! I was not about to end up in a Borneo jail, so it was full ahead for the next three hours. After we were well east of Tawau, I closed down one engine and engaged half speed on the other. The engines were doing well, but best not to push it!

Kee got to work on food as we were now very hungry after the activities of last night and this morning. Fuk was giving the number one engine a check over, and waiting for it to cool so he could change oil filters and refill with clean oil. Lee was sitting behind the wheelhouse, out of the sun, cleaning the weapons and recharging the magazines.

Chapter 12

Fire Fight

We reached Darvel Bay, heading for Lahad Datu to refuel.

"Jake! Jake!" It was Lee from behind the wheelhouse. "Two boats coming fast from the mangrove swamps – pirates!"

"Fuk, get clear of that engine fast."

"OK, Jake, fire it up," came the reply from below. Both engines were now running at full throttle, but we were still too heavy to outrun the two vessels closing fast.

"Lee, get all our smoke canisters and start dropping them into that open water barrel at the stern." Soon there were volumes of coloured smoke – green, yellow, red and blue – coming from the drum, and leaving a thick cloud to our rear. I turned ten degrees to port for five hundred yards, to spread the smoke and get the two following craft to head to port also. Now I came back ten degrees for five hundred yards and went twenty degrees to starboard. The area was well covered in smoke so I kept going to starboard, working my way round behind the two vessels. "Lee, stop making smoke. Stand by for a fire fight."

We came round behind the smoke, and to our surprise there was no sign of the two vessels – they had entered the smoke. I slowed down, waiting for the smoke to start to clear, and then we saw the first one through the haze, rear end on. We opened fire first, catching them looking the other way. I opened the engines and picked up speed, not wanting the other vessel to suddenly emerge from the smoke and catch us idle in the water. There was much screaming and shouting as our guns and grenades ripped through the pirate vessel, already burning from end to end.

The second vessel came into view ahead of us, and all fire switched to that vessel as she came head onto us. Rounds crashed into our wheelhouse and Kee went down, but got to his feet – he had blood streaming from an arm wound. Lee raked the vessel with the twin machine guns and Fuk was firing grenades, scoring two hits as I turned to port to avoid collision. Pirates were jumping into burning oil, floating on the sea, screaming. Fuk and Lee finished them off as I slowed and stopped, and turned my attention to Kee. The bullet had passed through his arm, missing the bone. Kee just grinned as I applied a dressing. Lee shouted, "There must have been about twenty men."

"Jake, over there – three in the water – must have been the first to jump overboard."

"Let's get them on board before the sharks get them. I want information." We came alongside the survivors and dragged them on board. Lee and Fuk bound them while I covered them with my rifle. One of them had a broken arm, and bone was showing, blood running down his side. The second man had a head wound, but not bad. Both men were dressed in shirts and sarongs, but the third was dressed in what had been a white shirt, slacks and leather sandals. I was curious about this character – he looked to be in authority.

"Lee, take those three to the stern and interrogate the bastards; find out who this guy is."

"OK, boss, we interrogate them." They were dragged to the stern screaming for mercy. It was not long before Lee returned to inform me that "The one in the white shirt is their boss – 'The Crow'." I'd thought so.

I went with Lee to the stern. "So you're 'The Crow'? Who are you working for? Mr Yew? Is that correct?" No answer. "You speak English?" Again, no answer. Lee bounced his rifle butt off his toes, and there were screams of pain, and then a torrent of four letter words poured forth in English. "Ah, we do speak English then!"

"I tell you nothing," he shouted.

"Fuk, throw the one with the broken arm overboard." The man was grabbed and thrown overboard screaming. "You want to talk now? Fuk, throw the other one back into the sea, the sharks won't be long." Now 'The Crow' was looking worried, but still not talking. Then the screaming started from the two in the water – they had spotted the sharks closing in. "Lee, shoot the sharks and keep them away till this guy starts talking. Fuk, go and get your pig skin and wrap this bastard in it."

'The Crow' was sweating profusely – there was terror in his face. How many women, children and innocent people going about their lawful business had he tortured and murdered? Kee appeared with the pig skin. "We make deal," he said in good English."

"Ah, he speaks! You have nothing to trade. Kee, wrap that skin around him."

"OK, I work for Mr Yew. He wants me to spy on you at first, and then he wants me to get men and attack you. We did not think you would be armed. I was surprised."

"Wonders! What magic there is in pigskin?" I said. "Was it one of your boats that attacked us up river from Kalabakan?"

"Ah, yes! We were concerned when they did not return to Tawau, and your boat did not return either. At first we though we had missed you, then we got reports from fishermen who saw you passing Tawau. We assumed you would head for Lahad Datu across Darvel Bay, so I went by the road to Kunak to organise a crew. We had no reason to think that you were armed."

"Just as well we were, or you would have killed us." He stood there, grinning at us. "What is this all about? Why you have so many guns? What are you carrying? I pay you plenty money to let me go."

"How much?"

"$10,000 … $20,000 … you take me to my camp to collect." I raised my rifle and squeezed the trigger. The rounds went right through

'The Crow', throwing him over the stern in a shower of blood and bone. The sharks were fast to attack with all this blood in the water. "OK, let's get underway." The engines roared into life and we departed the scene. Lee patched up Kee with a new dressing and gave him an injection to stop any infection. Fuk came up from the galley with curry and rice and a gallon of coffee. Once we had finished our meal we set to work, filling the holes in the wheelhouse and slapping on paint, as we did not want anyone thinking we had been in a war. All weapons were now below decks and we looked just like a fishing trip once again.

By the time we got to Sandakan we were almost out of fuel and the fresh water was now gone. "I hope there are no more attacks, Lee! It's going to be a long journey around Sabah to Labuan."

"Hope the weather holds, Jake. We will be going through the typhoon area – the winds come down from the high mountains and churn up the sea into water spouts, hence the name – 'the land below the wind'.

Next morning we entered the harbour of Sandakan. It was full of shipping, mostly loading timber. We headed for a fuelling point and started to fill up, including the drums on deck. We found two had bullet holes in them, so we dumped them in a skip and helped ourselves to replacements. Kee was filling the water tank with drinking water till it overflowed. Water bottles and plastic containers were filled, and we all had showers. Kee and Fuk went off to buy food from a local trader, and soon the galley and our dining area were full. A new wok and cooking pots were acquired from a shop in the harbour area to replace the damaged ones, now dumped in the skip. Lee went ashore and phoned Mai Ling to update her on all that had happened, and make arrangements for the DC3 to move to Kuching. She was worried but would contact the pilots and brief them about the change in plans.

"OK, Lee. The boat is low in the water, but it'll be all right as long as the weather holds and we don't run into trouble." Lee cast off at the bow and Fuk cast off at the rear, under the eye of the local policeman who was watching us closely, but we avoided eye contact.

Soon we were out to the open sea, and land was just a line on the horizon to port. Then the rain started and lasted for more than twenty-four hours. Visibility was down to fifty yards – so one eye was on the radar, the other on the compass. The pumps were working overtime, keeping the bilge water at a safe level, although we were struggling at one point to keep ahead! If the pumps had failed we would have gone down – I had no doubt about that. The rain stopped and then the sea was as calm as a mill pound.

We made a few night stops in mangrove swamps to rest and carry out servicing work on the engines. The boat was now riding higher in the water as we had burnt up fuel and used water – we were making good time. Food packing and waste was dumped; we found it was now easy to move about the boat without falling over boxes of food and bags of rice. We saw fishing boats going about their business but they took no notice of us.

We arrived at Labuan late on a Friday afternoon as the sun was setting; we found a berth on a pontoon in mid harbour. There was plenty of activity here – boats of every size and shape – junks to super tankers and container ships, all loading and unloading. We spotted a refuelling barge and asked it to come alongside and fuel us up.

When it was dark, Lee and I went ashore to enquire about Mr Yew, and soon found out he had been away on business but was now back in town. We were directed to his home by a shopkeeper. "He very rich man, big house and armed guards, two women live with him," said the shopkeeper.

"Is he married?" I asked.

"No, he not married, just have bom bom girls." We laughed and the shopkeeper joined in, handing us a Coke each. "Ah, you want bom bom girls? I get for you, never been touched, very young!" "Sorry, old man. That's not what we are here for," I said. "I get you good deal – big discount all night." It was time for us to go so we purchased two cases of Coke and returned to the harbour, signalling to the *Dragon*. Kee came over in the dinghy to collect us, and it was not long till we turned in for the night.

Motor Junk Dragon

My friend Fuk Yew armed with LMG

Inside Jap bunker

Map with Battle with Pirates at Darvil Bay,
route in and out of Tawau and Area of the Bunker all marked

Battle in Darvil Bay
pirate vessel burning

Jake takes a rest at the entrance to tunnel with some of the gold,
September 1994

Gold Bars

Tunnel

Chapter 13

The End Game

After a good breakfast, Lee and I headed for the bank. Mr Yew greeted us like lost kin. "Tea, coffee, cold drinks? Nice to see you again. I have been away on business, and work here just piles up. Brought me some gold have you?"

"No. We ran into some trouble before we could recover all of it and had to abort the mission. Pirates attacked us. We had to dump most of our equipment and run for it in a hail of gunfire. Now we need money to finance a new mission and carry out repairs to the boat."

"Oh, I see. I could do with some funds too. So much expense these days! How much do you need?"

"Same as before – cash – US bucks," said Lee.

I was watching Mr Yew very closely, and I could not tell if he had had any confirmation from his men in Tawau about what had happened. "What's in it for me?"

"How about ten bars for yourself – you get us cash and we can arrange for you to get ten bars tonight. We have it here in Labuan. You bring your car to the harbour and we load the gold. Better still, we eat first on board the *Dragon* and talk money."

"Yes, that sounds good to me. I get my driver to collect me at seven p.m. Now I get your cash." His hand reached for the buzzer and a young man came into the office. Mr Yew handed the attendant a request for the cash; he left the office and returned ten minutes later. Lee placed it in his backpack and thanked Mr Yew.

I was getting concerned about Mr Yew coming to our boat, and could not wait to get out of this bank and find out what Lee was playing at. Outside, and heading back to the harbour, I asked Lee what that had been all about. "Jake, I have a plan. Let me explain ..."

At seven p.m., Lee went over to the jetty to meet Mr Yew, expecting him only to be with his driver. But there were two more passengers in the car – Mr Yew had his two women with him. I was furious at this, but we could do nothing but welcome them on board. I pulled Lee to one side and told him to go back to the jetty and invite the driver too – we wanted no loose ends.

"I thought you would like some company, maybe some entertainment?"

"Thank you, Mr Yew," I said. Shit! We had not considered this, but we were stuck with the situation now. We all sat round the mess room table, drinking while Kee prepared the meal. Meanwhile, the girls had their hands over everyone. Little did Mr Yew know he was sitting on top of the gold! By the time the food arrived, Mr Yew and the girls were well on their way to being drunk. The food was excellent – although drugged for our guests – and Mr Yew was praising the cook. Then Kee passed round more drinks to our guests, laced with sleeping pills. Kee invited the driver to see our engine room, and off they went laughing and joking. It was not long before our guests were sleeping soundly. Kee returned alone from the engine room, grinning from ear to ear, waving the driver's Colt 45 about.

"The driver is sleeping sound down there, no mess," said Kee.

"Let's get underway before anyone gets interested in that abandoned car," I said. Soon we were clear of the harbour, and heading west with a tail wind. The dawn was about to break behind us and it was already getting light. An hour later we were far out from land when Kee and Lee dragged the unconscious driver on deck, shortly followed by the women and Mr Yew. I did not know what was intended now. Fuk and Kee started to tie rope to their ankles – the end of the rope was tied to an anchor! We were still doing about ten knots, when Kee lowered the anchor over the back end and let go. I watched as a hundred feet of rope ran out, then there was a jerk and the driver went over first, quickly followed by the two women and Mr Yew last. All four bodies disappeared into the deep of the South China Sea!

That night, after the evening meal, Lee emptied the four hundred thousand US dollars on the table. Kee and Fuk looked on in amazement, not knowing how Lee had screwed Mr Yew. Lee divided the money into four and placed a pile in front of each of us. "Just a little bonus to be going on with. Who said crime doesn't pay?" I was starting to feel like a pirate myself now but had to consider that, if the boot was on the other foot, Mr Yew would not have hesitated in having all of us disposed of. He had tried, and failed.

Susie came to mind as I stood alone in the wheelhouse – something she had said a long time ago. "All expendable – that is how it is here. Get used to it, Jake." I smiled to myself as I looked westward across a flat sea, with the sun climbing high behind me. The deck was already getting hot. I went below for breakfast and looked around the mess room; it was as if we had never had any guests, no evidence, just like a dream.

We headed on towards Sarawak and the mouth of the river that would take us up to Kuching. We had no further encounters with pirates for the rest of our journey, although we were starting to look and feel like pirates ourselves. We entered the river for the run up to Kuching, and after a short time it came into sight. We managed to berth alongside the jetty. Lee went off to phone, and it wasn't long before Mai Ling arrived, driving a hire car, followed by the two Australian pilots in a truck.

We all greeted each other, and then started to unload empty boxes from the truck and take them on board. Lee and the other two stayed below decks, packing the bars and sealing the boxes. The boxes came up on deck, one at a time, as soon at they were ready to go on the truck.

"Bloody heavy, mate!"

"Must've been doing a lot of digging, mate. I think you must be trying to steal half of Borneo!"

"Just artefacts for the museum in Singapore. You must visit it sometime!" I said.

"No, thanks mate. I like cold beer and hot girls."

Once the boxes were loaded, Mai Ling and I drove to the airport, while Lee and the other two took the *Dragon* down river on her last journey. I felt sad to leave her – she had served us well. Lee took her offshore, lowered the inflatable, and then scuttled the *Dragon*. The three of them returned up river at speed, stopping short of Kuching in the mangrove swamps, slashing the inflatable and letting it sink, then made their way into town, and took a taxi out to the airport. Mai Ling had clean clothes and showers arranged for us, and it wasn't long before we looked respectable once again.

The good old DC3 was loaded and ready for take-off, as Mai Ling said, "I have had those papers you found translated. There was a Jap concentration camp close by the rail line that was never completed, but was intended to link the camp with the river. The camp was operated by the Kempei Tai, with their guards. The gold was going to be shipped to West Mindanao in the Philippines for storage."

We were lifting off the runway. I watched the land drop away as the old aircraft struggled to gain height under its load. "So, tell us why the camp was there and never found, Mai Ling?"

"From what I understand, most of the prisoners were from Tarakan and Surabaya in Dutch Borneo – Dutch oil workers, planters and local people – there with plenty of money, and all the gold looted from the banks, as well as gold rings, ornaments, dentures and fillings. General Yamishita has signed one of the papers ordering the collection of all gold and valuables. It was intended that these would vanish without trace. What better place than far up a jungle river, with no towns or villages and no means of escape. Allied prisoners were taken from

Sandakan to work on the camp and railway. When the allies landed in 1945 at Tarakan to recapture Borneo, the Kempei Tai must have killed off all the prisoners – British, Australian and Dutch, probably their own guards too – and then tried to escape the allies, with the intention of returning after the war for the gold. Events overtook them and, more likely, they were taken prisoner and executed, or killed by the head hunters as they tried to escape. So no one knows about the camp, or the gold. The Kempei Tai were well linked to the Yakusa – the Japanese mafia.

"Other papers list more than a hundred sites that are located in the Philippines. I found this other article about unknown caves and Japanese spoils, which, according to an American columnist, could be worth more than US $100 billion and distributed over 172 hiding places on land and sea."

I fell into a deep sleep as Mai Ling talked to the others. She didn't wake me until we were approaching Singapore, a few hours later. I awoke, looked at Mai Ling and said, "It's been a great adventure and I wouldn't have missed it for the world, but I think I've had enough adventure for a lifetime. We all have plenty – and all of us are still in good health. I only wish Chalky, Sunshine, Susie and Ruby had been in at the end to share what we have." Mai Ling lent forward and patted my hand. There was a tear in her eye.

Postscript

Kee got his rubber plantation in Malaysia, married and had five sons.

Fuk got his girly bars and brothels in Penang but he was soon closed down. Now he has a fishing boat taking tourists fishing, or so I'm told.

Lee still lives with his mother Mai Ling and is very prominent in the gold market in Singapore.

Jake returned to the Philippines, married and now has a daughter. He settled down on his plantation and spends much of his time looking into the mysteries of Yamashita's missing gold and the alleged sites on land and sea.

Every soldier has a story to tell – this one's mine

The Author enlisted into the Queens Own Cameron Highlanders in 1958. He served in Malaya, Singapore, Brunei, Borneo, Aden and Western Europe. If you served in the Far Easst then this is for you, if not then see what you missed.

What the literary Consultants say:

Mr Jacobs' colourful memoir is an excellent testament to his time spent in the military and is certainly an exciting read. Full of authentic flavour with both military and exotic foreign adventures. Not for the faint hearted. A no holds barred treatment of a particularly interesting period and a wonderful record of this courageous, and witty and entertaining individual.

Another unusual feature of this work is that it is a very good mix of fact and fiction. This is an enticing and intriguing mix and the reader is encouraged to imagine for himself which parts actually took place and which are the product of the author's fertile imagination. So cogent and coherent is the book that it is virtually impossible to determine fact from fiction and this is certainly a sign of the book's strength. The reader will remain hooked and totally under the author's powerful spell from beginning to end.